HAZOP AND HAZAN

Identifying and Assessing Process Industry Hazards

Third Edition

Trevor Kletz

INSTITUTION OF CHEMICAL ENGINEERS

Distributed exclusively in the USA and Canada by
Hemisphere Publishing Corporation

Published by
Institution of Chemical Engineers
Davis Building
165–171 Railway Terrace
Rugby, Warwickshire CV21 3HQ, UK.

Distributed exclusively in the USA and Canada by
Hemisphere Publishing Corporation
A member of the Taylor & Francis Group
1900 Frost Road, Suite 101
Bristol
PA 19007
USA.

ISBN 0 85295 285 6
First Edition 1983
Second Edition 1986
Third Edition 1992

ISBN 1 56032 276 4 Hemisphere Publishing Corporation

Library of Congress Cataloging-in-Publication Data
Kletz, Trevor A.
Hazop and hazan: identifying and assessing process industry hazards / Trevor Kletz. – 3rd ed.
Includes bibliographic references and index,
ISBN 1–56032–276–4
1. Chemical engineering–Safety measures.
TP149.K62 1992 92–5475
660′.2804–dc20 CIP

Printed by Redwood Press Limited, Melksham, Wiltshire.

FOREWORD

The Institution of Chemical Engineers' example syllabus for chemical engineering education[1] includes 'Systematic identification and quantification of hazards, hazard and operability studies' and this book is intended to spread knowledge of these subjects.

It is based on lecture notes that I have used for several years for teaching these subjects to undergraduate and graduate students, to mature students attending short courses on loss prevention and to former colleagues attending in-house courses in industry. University departments of chemical engineering may therefore find the book useful. It may also be useful for in-house courses in industry. It is not intended as a handbook for experts.

A few suggestions on the presentation of the material may be helpful.

Chapter 1 puts the material in context and can form an introduction to the first session of a course.

Chapter 2 deals with identification of hazards by hazard and operability studies (hazop) and requires at least two hours. It could be presented as a lecture in one hour but it is better if those present can complete the various columns in Table 2.2, the lecturer (or discussion leader) writing them down on a board as they do so. The group must, of course, be allowed to come to different conclusions than those in the Table if they wish to do so. There is no right answer. The group may consider that those who drew up Table 2.2 went too far or did not go far enough, and the group could be right.

If possible the group should not exceed 20 people; the fewer the better, as long as at least five or six are present.

Chapter 3 deals with the quantification of hazards by hazard analysis (hazan) and requires at least three hours. Mature students seem able to take three hours at a stretch, but not undergraduates!

Chapter 4 describes some of the points to look for when reading hazard analyses carried out by others. It is intended for mature students.

Chapter 5 briefly discusses some of the objections that have been raised to hazop and hazan. It is also intended for mature students.

Chapter 6 gives a few notes on sources of data and confidence limits.

Chapter 7 gives a brief history of hazop and hazan.

The subjects discussed in this book and many other aspects of loss prevention are treated more extensively in F.P. Lees' *Loss Prevention in the Process Industries*, 2 volumes, Butterworths, 1980, especially Chapters 7–9 (referred to in later pages as *Lees*).

Thanks are due to the many colleagues who provided ideas for this book or commented on the draft and to the Science and Engineering Research Council for financial support.

Thanks are also due to the American Institute of Chemical Engineers and Dr H.G. Lawley for permission to quote Table 2.2, to Mr J.E. Gillett for permission to quote Tables 5.1 and 5.2, and to Applied Science Publishers for permission to quote much of the material in Chapter 4 which originally appeared in *Reliability Engineering*.

For this new edition I have corrected a few misprints, added a few words of additional explanation here and there (especially in Sections 3.4 and 5.3 and in Chapters 6 and 7) and included some new references and some examples of accidents that could have been prevented by hazop. A set of slides on the subject of this book, large copies of the diagrams suitable for making into overhead projector transparencies and notes on their use are available from the Institution of Chemical Engineers.

To avoid the clumsy phrases 'he or she' and 'him or her' I have used 'he' and 'him'. Though there has been a welcome increase in the number of women employed in the process industries the manager, designer and accident victim are still usually male.

REFERENCE

1. *First degree course including guidelines on accreditation of degree courses*, January 1989, Institution of Chemical Engineers, Rugby, UK, Section 2.3.1.

CONTENTS

		PAGE
FOREWORD		iii
1.	**HAZARD IDENTIFICATION AND ASSESSMENT**	1
1.1	Introduction	1
1.2	A Note On Nomenclature	4
2.	**HAZARD AND OPERABILITY STUDIES (HAZOP)**	7
2.1	What Is A Hazop?	7
2.2	Who Carries Out A Hazop?	15
2.3	When Is A Hazop Carried Out And How Long Does It Take?	18
2.4	Some Points To Watch During Hazop	20
2.5	An Example Of A Hazop	24
2.6	Could A Computer Carry Out A Hazop?	26
2.7	The Limitations Of Hazop	29
2.8	'Do We Need To Hazop This Plant?' 'It Is Only A Simple Project' Or 'It Is Similar To The Last One'	32
2.9	The Use Of Quantitative Methods During Hazop	34
2.10	The Use Of Hazop In Other Industries	35
2.11	Conclusion	37
APPENDIX TO CHAPTER 2 — SOME ACCIDENTS THAT COULD HAVE BEEN PREVENTED BY HAZARD AND OPERABILITY STUDIES		39
A2.1	Reverse Flow	39
A2.2	Bhopal	39
A2.3	A Fire In A Water Sump	40
A2.4	A Protective Device That Did Not Work	41
A2.5	Services And Modifications: Two Neglected Areas	41
A2.6	A Computer-Controlled Batch Reaction	43
A2.7	Abbeystead: An Explosion In A Water Pumping Station	44
A2.8	The Sellafield Leak	45
A2.9	Formation Of Separate Layers	48
A2.10	A Hazard Not Foreseen By Hazop	50

3.	**HAZARD ANALYSIS (HAZAN)**	52
3.1	Objective	52
3.2	Why Do We Want To Apply Numerical Methods To Safety Problems?	52
3.3	The Stages Of Hazard Analysis	54
3.4	Some Of The Targets Or Criteria	56
3.5	Estimating How Often An Incident Will Occur	71
3.6	Pitfalls In Hazard Analysis	84
3.7	The Man Or Woman In The Middle	93
3.8	Examples Of Hazard Analysis	95
3.9	A Summary Of The Main Sources Of Error In Hazard Analysis	100
3.10	A Final Note	100

APPENDIX TO CHAPTER 3 — BELT AND BRACES 103

4.	**A MANAGER'S GUIDE TO HAZARD ANALYSIS**	106
4.1	Introduction	106
4.2	Arithmetic, Algebra And Units	106
4.3	The Model	107
4.	The Unforeseen Hazards	108
4.5	The Assumptions	109
4.6	Data	109
4.7	Human Reliability	111
4.8	Recommendations	112
4.9	Comparison With Experience	113
4.10	Closed Shop Or Open Shop?	113

5.	**OBJECTIONS TO HAZOP AND HAZAN**	114
5.1	Objections To Hazop	114
5.2	Technical Objections To Hazan	115
5.3	Popular Objections To Hazan	121

APPENDIX TO CHAPTER 5 — LIMITATIONS ON THE APPLICATION OF QUANTITATIVE METHODS TO RAILWAY TRAVEL 128

6.	**SOURCES OF DATA AND CONFIDENCE LIMITS**	130
6.1	Data Banks And Data Books	130

6.2 If Failure Has Never Occurred 131
6.3 Confidence Limits 131
6.4 Data On Mechanical Equipment May Be Data On People 132

7. THE HISTORY OF HAZOP AND HAZAN 134
7.1 Hazop 134
7.2 Hazan 138

CONCLUSIONS 141

ADDENDUM — AN ATLAS OF SAFETY THINKING 142

INDEX 146

NOTE

The Library and Information Service of the Institution of Chemical Engineers in Rugby, UK, offers a worldwide service for the supply of the references listed in this book.

1. HAZARD IDENTIFICATION AND ASSESSMENT

'The great end of life is not knowledge but action.'
T.H. Huxley (1825–1895)

1.1 INTRODUCTION

The techniques for identifying hazards — for finding out what hazards are present in a plant or process — and the techniques for assessing those hazards — for deciding how far we ought to go in removing the hazards or protecting people from them — are often confused. Figure 1.1 may help to make the differences clear.

The left-hand side shows some of the methods used for identifying hazards — and problems that make operation difficult.

Some hazards and problems are obvious. For example, if we manufacture ethylene oxide by mixing oxygen and ethylene close to the explosive limit we do not need a special technique to tell us that if we get the proportions wrong there may be a big bang.

The traditional method of identifying hazards — in use from the dawn of technology until the present day — was to build the plant and see what happens — 'every dog is allowed one bite'. Until it bites someone, we can say that we did not know it would. This is not a bad method when the size of an incident is limited but is no longer satisfactory now that we keep dogs which may be as big as Bhopal (over 2000 killed in one bite) or even Flixborough (28 killed). We need to identify hazards before the accidents occur.

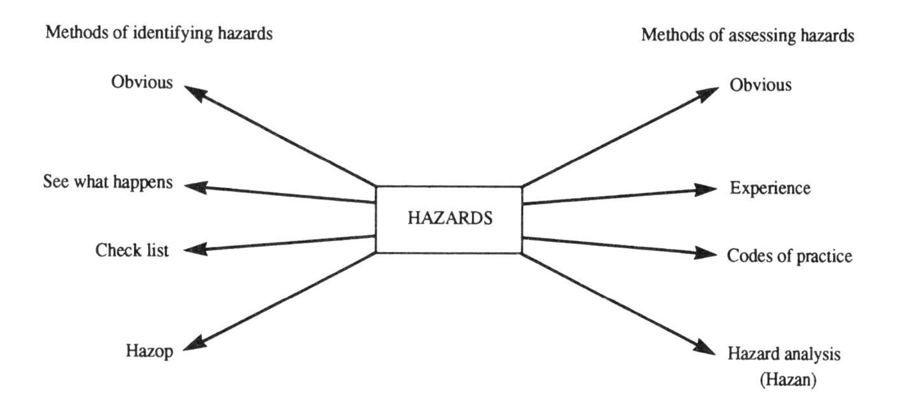

Figure 1.1 Methods of identifying and assessing hazards.

Check lists are often used to identify hazards but their disadvantage is that items not on the list are not brought forward for consideration and our minds are closed to them. Check lists may be satisfactory if there is little or no innovation and all the hazards have been met before, but are least satisfactory when the design is new.

For this reason the process industries have come to prefer the more creative or open-ended technique known as a hazard and operability study or hazop. It is described in Chapter 2. It is now widely used on designs for new plants and plant extensions but, because of the effort involved, has been less widely used on existing plants.

Samuel Coleridge described history as a 'lantern on the stern', illuminating the hazards the ship has passed through rather than those that lie ahead. It is better to illuminate the hazards we have passed through than not illuminate them at all, as we may pass the same way again, but we should try to see them before we meet them. Hazop can be a lantern on the bow.

Unfortunately we do not always learn from the hazards we have passed through, but that is outside the scope of this book[1,2].

Other methods of identifying hazards are described in *Lees*, Chapter 8. Some of them (see Section 2.7), such as screening tests and hazard indices, are intended for use during the early stages of a project, before design starts, while others such as pre-commissioning checks, come later. These methods — like hazop — have been developed to match the increasing complexity of modern plants.

After we have identified the hazards we have to decide how far to go in removing them or in protecting people and property. Some of the methods used are listed on the right-hand side of Figure 1.1. Sometimes there is a cheap and obvious way of removing the hazard, sometimes our experience or a code of practice tell us what to do. Sometimes it is less easy to decide. We can then try to work out the probability of an accident and the extent of the consequences and compare them with a target or criterion. This method is called hazard analysis or hazan in this book. Sometimes a 5-minute estimation is sufficient. On other occasions detailed studies can take many weeks.

Hazop can and should be applied to all new designs, unless we are making an exact copy of an existing plant which has been proved satisfactory, as we need to know all the hazards and all the problems that can prevent efficient operation. Hazan on the other hand should be used selectively — there are neither the need, the data nor the resources to attempt to quantify every problem on every plant. Carling[3] has described a hazop which produced 326 recommendations of which only seven justified a detailed hazard analysis.

In the development of a design the hazard and operability study comes first. We identify the hazards and the problems that prevent efficient operation and then decide what to do about them. However, if there is an obvious major hazard we may start on the hazard analysis before the hazard and operability study is carried out. In a hazard and operability study the operability part is as important as the hazard part. In most studies more operating problems are identified than hazards.

Hazop and hazan are often confused. Figure 1.1 and Table 1.1 should make the difference clear. However, if someone asks you to carry out a hazop or hazan on a design, first make sure that the questioner is clear on the difference.

The techniques described in later chapters are sophisticated techniques which enable companies to use their resources more effectively. They assume that the general level of management is competent, that the plant will be operated and maintained in the manner assumed by the design team and in accordance with good management and engineering practice. In particular they assume that protective systems will be tested regularly and repaired promptly when necessary.

If these assumptions are not true then hazop and hazan are a waste of time. It is no use identifying hazards or estimating their probability if no-one wants to do anything about them; it is no use installing trips and alarms if no-one is going to use or maintain them. The time spent on a hazop and hazan would be better spent on bringing the safety consciousness of employees and management up to standard. Atallah and Gazman have described techniques that can be used to do this in developing countries[4].

TABLE 1.1
The differences between hazop and hazan

Hazop	Hazan
Identifies hazards	Assesses hazards
Preferred technique: use on every project	Selective technique: use when others fail
Qualitative	Quantitative
Done by a team	Done by one or two people
Also called: 'What if?'	Also called: Risk analysis Risk assessment Probabilistic risk assessment (PRA) Quantitative risk assessment (QRA)

If you wish to introduce hazop and/or hazan into an organisation in which they have not been used before, you should start small. Do not try to set up a large team capable of studying all new and existing designs. Instead apply the methods to one or two problems. If your colleagues find that the methods are useful they will ask for more and the use of the techniques will grow. If, on the other hand, the methods do not suit your organisation, little has been lost.

Despite all our efforts we shall fail to foresee every hazard and some will result in accidents. We should learn from these accidents, not only from those that result in serious injury or damage but also from those that do not — for example, leaks that do not ignite. If these 'near-misses' are not investigated and the lessons made known to those concerned, next time injury or damage may result.

In my former company, ICI, hazop and hazan form part of a series of six hazard studies carried out on new projects as they progress[5]. They are:

(1) Exploratory phase: Identification of basic hazards and assessment of suitability of possible sites.

(2) Flowsheet phase: Identification and assessment of significant hazards, using hazard analysis.

(3) Detailed design: Hazard and operability study.

(4) Construction: A check that decisions made in earlier studies have been implemented.

(5) Commissioning: Final inspection.

(6) Post-commissioning: Safety audit and review of modifications.

It seems from this list that the assessment of hazards is carried out in Study 2 before the hazards have been identified by hazop in Study 3! However, the obvious hazards should be assessed as soon as possible. The hazop will identify other hazards, most of which will be assessed qualitatively during the hazop, but some of which will have to be assessed outside the meeting by hazard analysis.

1.2 A NOTE ON NOMENCLATURE

Hazard analysis has several other names (Table 1.1). When I wrote my first paper on the use of quantitative methods of assessing risks in the chemical industry[6] I started by using the term 'risk analysis'. Then I realised that ICI had sponsored a book entitled *Risk analysis*[7] which described methods of assessing the commercial risks of a project. I therefore introduced the term 'hazard analysis' instead, but other writers often use 'risk analysis'.

In an attempt to standardise nomenclature the Institution of Chemical Engineers has published a guide[8]. They suggest that 'hazard analysis' is used to

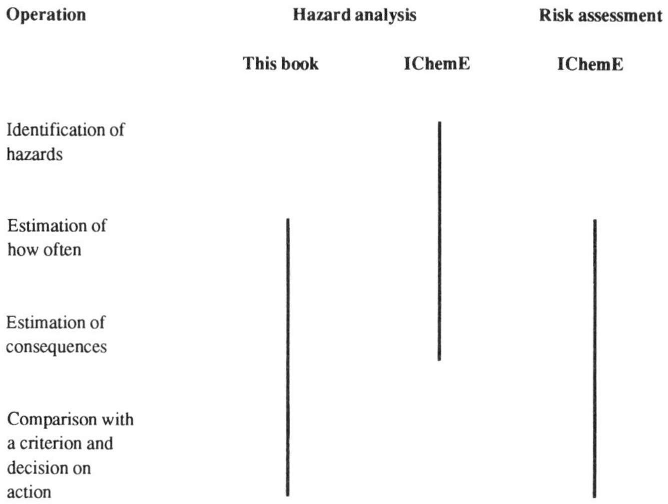

Operation **Hazard analysis** **Risk assessment**

This book **IChemE** **IChemE**

Identification of hazards

Estimation of how often

Estimation of consequences

Comparison with a criterion and decision on action

Figure 1.2 Some definitions compared. Quantified risk assessment (QRA) and probabilistic risk assessment (PRA) are usually synonyms for 'hazard analysis', as used in this book, but the terms may be widened to include the identification of hazards.

describe methods of identifying hazards and estimating the probability and consequences of an incident but that it should exclude the crucial final step of deciding what should be done about them (see Chapter 3). They suggest that what I call hazard analysis (or hazan) should be called 'risk assessment'.

Many writers, particularly in the US, call it 'quantified (or quantitative) risk assessment' (QRA) or 'probabilistic risk assessment' (PRA) and the former term is now used by the UK Health and Safety Executive[9].

I have nevertheless continued to use 'hazard analysis' in the same sense as I used it in the first edition of this book because the term is still widely used with this meaning and because its contraction, hazan, contrasts conveniently with hazop. (*Hazop and risk assessment* would not be a good title for this book.) Figure 1.2 summarises the different ways in which the various terms are used.

There is general agreement that a 'hazard' is a substance, object or situation with a potential for an accident or damage and that a 'risk' is the likelihood that the accident or damage will occur.

REFERENCES IN CHAPTER 1

1. Kletz, T.A., 1980, Organisations have no memory, *Loss Prevention*, 13: 1.
2. Kletz, T.A., 1976, Accidents that will occur during the coming year, *Loss Prevention*, 10: 151.
3. Carling, N., Hazop study of BAPCO's FCCU complex, *American Petroleum Institute Committee on Safety and Fire Protection Spring Meeting, Denver, Colorado, 8-11 April 1986.*
4. Atallah, S. and Guzman, E., 1988, Safety audits in developing countries, *Symposium Series No. 110*, Institution of Chemical Engineers, Rugby, UK, 35.
5. Hawksley, J.L., *The Safety Practitioner*, October 1987, 10.
6. Kletz, T.A., 1971, Hazard analysis — a quantitive approach to safety, *Symposium Series No. 34*, Institution of Chemical Engineers, Rugby, UK, 75.
7. Imperial Chemical Industries Ltd, 1968, *Assessing projects: Book 5, Risk analysis*, Methuen, London.
8. *Nomenclature for hazard and risk assesment in the process industries*, 1985, Institution of Chemical Engineers, Rugby, UK.
9. Health and Safety Executive, 1989, *Quantified risk assessment: Its input to decision making*, HMSO, London.

2. HAZARD AND OPERABILITY STUDIES (HAZOP)

'Since the destruction of the Temple, the gift of prophecy has been denied to prophets and bestowed upon scholars.'
Rabbi Eudemus of Haifa

2.1 WHAT IS A HAZOP?

As I explained in Chapter 1, a hazard and operability study is the method recommended for identifying hazards and problems which prevent efficient operation. In what follows the technique is described as it would be applied to a continuous plant. Modifications of the technique, so that it can be applied to batch plants, are described only briefly (in Section 2.1.1). References 1 and 2 give more detail.

Hazop is a technique which provides opportunities for people to let their imaginations go free and think of all possible ways in which hazards or operating problems might arise, but — to reduce the chance that something is missed — it is done in a systematic way, each pipeline and each sort of hazard is considered in turn. The study is carried out by a team so that the members can stimulate each other and build upon each other's ideas.

A pipeline for this purpose is one joining two main plant items, for example, we might start with the line leading from the feed tank through the feed pump to the first feed heater. A series of guide words are applied to this line in turn. The words are:

NONE	PART OF
MORE OF	MORE THAN (or AS WELL AS)
LESS OFOTHER THAN	

NONE for example, means no forward flow or reverse flow when there should be forward flow. We ask:

- Could there be no flow?
- If so, how could it arise?
- What are the consequences of no flow?
- Are the consequences hazardous or do they prevent efficient operation?
- If so, can we prevent no flow (or protect against the consequences) by changing the design or method of operation?
- If so, does the size of the hazard or problem (that is, the severity of the consequences multiplied by the probability of occurrence) justify the extra expense?

The same questions are then applied to 'reverse flow' and we then move on to the next guide word, MORE OF. Could there be 'more flow' than design? If so, how could it arise? And so on. The same questions are asked about 'more pressure' and 'more temperature' and, if they are important, about other parameters such as 'more radioactivity' or 'more viscosity'. Table 2.1 summarises the meanings of the guide words while Figure 2.1 summarises the whole process.

When all the lines leading into a vessel have been studied, the guide word OTHER THAN is applied to the vessel. It is not essential to apply the other guide words to this item as any problems should come to light when the inlet and exit lines are studied. However, to reduce the chance that something is missed the guide words should be applied to any operation carried out in the vessel. For example, if settling takes place we ask if it is possible to have no settling, reverse settling (ie, mixing), more settling or less settling, and similarly for stirring, heating, cooling and any other operations (see Section 2.8.4).

TABLE 2.1
Deviations generated by each guide word

Guide word	Deviations
NONE	No forward flow when there should be, ie no flow or reverse flow.
MORE OF	More of any relevant physical property than there should be, eg higher flow (rate or total quantity), higher temperature, higher pressure, higher viscosity, etc.
LESS OF	Less of any relevant physical property than there should be, eg lower flow (rate or total quantity), lower temperature, lower pressure, etc.
PART OF	Composition of system different from what it should be, eg change in ratio of components, component missing, etc.
MORE THAN	More components present in the system than there should be, eg extra phase present (vapour, solid), impurities (air, water, acids, corrosion products), etc.
OTHER THAN	What else can happen apart from normal operation, eg start-up, shut-down, uprating, low rate running, alternative operation mode, failure of plant services, maintenance, catalyst change, etc.

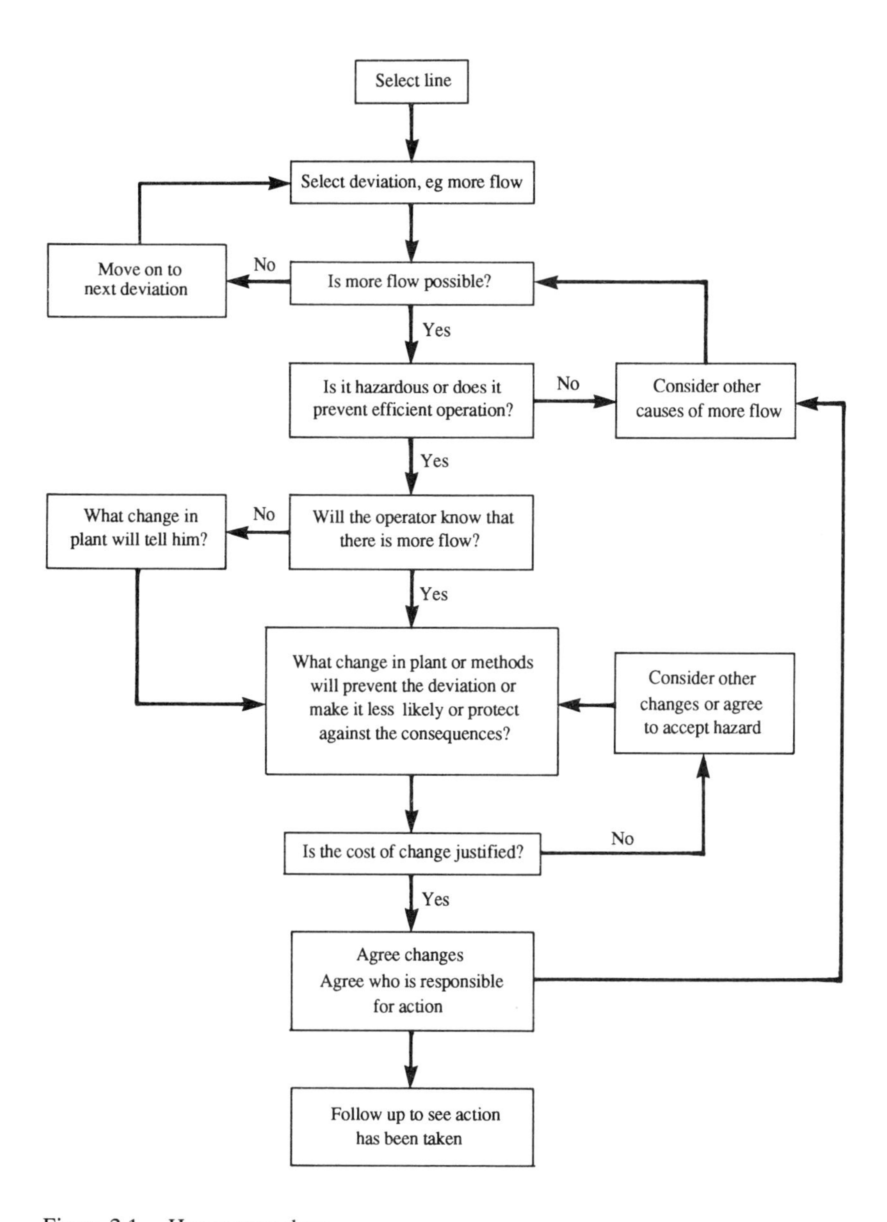

Figure 2.1 Hazop procedure.

The hazop also provides an opportunity to check that a number of detailed points have been considered during design. The team should ask:

- What types of gasket have been used? Should spiral wound ones be used? Has the number of types been kept to a minumum? (The more types we use, the greater the chance that the wrong sort will be used.)
- Has the number of types of nuts and bolts been kept to a minimum?
- Are the valves used of a type, such as rising spindle valves, whose position can be seen at a glance? If ball valves or cocks are used, can the handles be fitted in the wrong position?
- Are spectacle plates installed whenever regular slip-plating (blinding) of a joint (for maintenance or to prevent contamination) is foreseen?

Access is normally considered later in design, when a model of the plant (real or on computer) is available, but the hazop team should note any points that need special attention; for example, valves that will have to be operated frequently or in an emergency, and should therefore be easy to reach.

Ozog[17] describes a variation of the normal hazop procedure in which

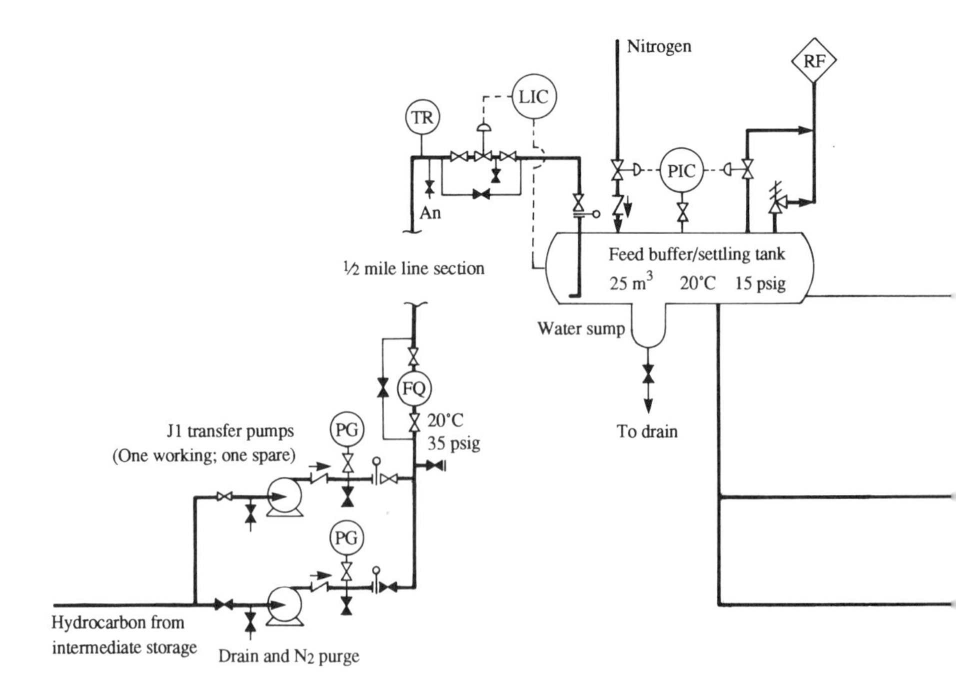

Figure 2.2 Feed section of proposed olefin dimerisation plant.

the guide words are applied to equipment (including pumps) instead of lines.

Start-up, shut-down and other abnormal conditions such as catalyst regeneration should be considered during hazop as well as normal operation.

Table 2.2 (see pages 12–13) describes in detail the results of a hazop on the plant shown in Figure 2.2. More details are given in Section 2.5. The procedure will become clearer as you go through each item in the table in turn. To get the most out of Table 2.2, Figure 2.2 should be displayed on a screen in front of the team, or copies given to each member, and everyone should be asked to carry out a hazop on it, the discussion leader acting as chairman. The results can then be compared with those in Table 2.2.

However, Table 2.2 should not be considered as the correct answer. Those taking part in the discussion may feel that the authors of Table 2.2 went too far, or did not go far enough, and they could be right.

Table 2.2 was based on a real study of an actual design. It is not a synthetic exercise, but it is written up in more detail than essential in a real life situation.

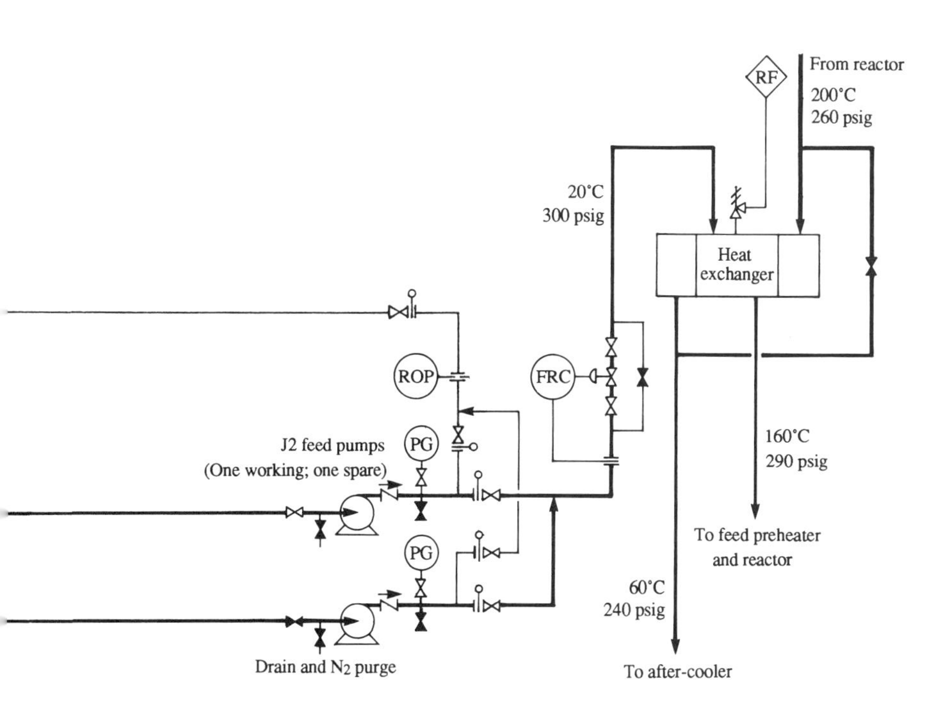

TABLE 2.2
Results of hazard and operability study of proposed olefin dimerisation unit: line section from intermediate storage to buffer/settling tank

Guide word	Deviation	Possible causes	Consequences	Action required
NONE	No flow	(1) No hydrocarbon available at intermediate storage.	Loss of feed to reaction section and reduced output. Polymer formed in heat exchanger under no flow conditions.	(a) Ensure good communications with intermediate storage operator. (b) Install low level alarm on settling tank LIC.
		(2) J1 pump fails (motor fault, loss of drive, impeller corroded away, etc).	As for (1).	Covered by (b).
		(3) Line blockage, isolation valve closed in error, or LCV fails shut.	As for (1). J1 pump overheats.	Covered by (b). (c) Install kickback on J1 pumps. (d) Check design of J1 pump strainers.
		(4) Line fracture.	As for (1). Hydrocarbon discharged into area adjacent to public highway.	Covered by (b). (e) Institute regular patrolling and inspection of transfer line.
MORE OF	More flow	(5) LCV fails open or LCV by-pass open in error.	Settling tank overfills.	(f) Install high level alarm on LIC and check sizing of relief opposite liquid overfilling. (g) Institute locking off procedure for LCV bypass when not in use.
			Incomplete separation of water phase in tank, leading to problems on reaction section.	(h) Extend J2 pump suction line to 12" above tank base.
	More pressure	(6) Isolation valve closed in error or LCV closes, with J1 pump running.	Transfer line subjected to full pump delivery or surge pressure.	(j) Covered by (c) except when kickback blocked or isolated. Check line, FQ and flange ratings and reduce stroking speed of LCV if necessary. Install a PG upstream of LCV and an independent PG on settling tank.

TABLE 2.2 (continued)

Guide word	Deviation	Possible causes	Consequences	Action required
		(7) Thermal expansion in an isolated valved section due to fire or strong sunlight.	Line fracture or flange lead.	(k) Install thermal expansion relief on valved section (relief discharge route to be decided later in study).
	More temperature	(8)High intermediate storage temperature.	Higher pressure in transfer line and settling tank.	(l) Check whether there is adequate warning of high temperature at intermediate storage. If not, install.
LESS OF	Less flow	(9) Leaking flange of valved stub not blanked and leaking.	Material loss adjacent to public highway.	Covered by (e) and the checks in (j).
	Less temperature	(10) Winter conditions.	Water sump and drain line freeze up.	(m) Lag water sump down to drain valve and steam trace drain valve and drain line downstream.
PART OF	High water concentration in stream	(11) High water level in intermediate storage tank.	Water sump fills up more quickly. Increased chance of water phase passing to reaction section.	(n) Arrange for frequent draining off of water from intermediate storage tank. Install high interface level alarm on sump.
	High concentration of lower alkanes or alkenes in stream	(12) Disturbance on distillation columns upstream of intermediate storage.	Higher system pressure.	(p) Check that design of settling tank and associated pipework, including relief valve sizing, will cope with sudden ingress of more volatile hydrocarbons.
MORE THAN	Organic acids present	(13) As for (12)	Increased rate of corrosion of tank base, sump and drain line.	(q) Check suitabillity of materials of construction.
OTHER	Maintenance	(14) Equipment failure, flange leak, etc.	Line cannot be completely drained or purged.	(r) Install low-point drain and N_2 purge point downstream of LCV. Also N_2 vent on settling tank.

2.1.1 BATCH PROCESSES

In studying a batch plant it is necessary to apply the guide words to the instructions as well as to the pipelines. For example, if an instruction states that 1 tonne of A has to be charged to a reactor, the team should consider deviations such as:

DON'T CHARGE A
CHARGE MORE A
CHARGE LESS A
CHARGE AS WELL AS A
CHARGE PART OF A (if A is a mixture)
CHARGE OTHER THAN A
REVERSE CHARGE A (that is, can flow occur from the reactor to the A container?) This can be the most serious deviation (see Appendix A2.1)
A IS ADDED EARLY
A IS ADDED LATE
A IS ADDED TOO QUICKLY
A IS ADDED TOO SLOWLY

Delay in adding reactants or carrying out subsequent operations can have serious results. For example, the explosion at Seveso in 1976[18] occurred because a reactor was left to stand for the weekend part way through a batch. Reference 19 describes another example.

As in the hazop of a continuous plant, we should also ask what will happen if temperature or pressure (or any other parameter of importance) deviates from the design intention.

There are further details in References 1 and 2.

Batch-type operations that are carried out on a continuous plant — for example, conditioning of equipment or catalyst change — should be studied in a similar way by listing the sequence of operations and applying the guide words to each step.

On computer-controlled plants the instructions to the computer (the applications software) should be studied as well as the line diagrams. For example, if the computer is instructed to take a certain action when a temperature rises, the team should consider the possible consequences of this action as well as the consequences of the computer failing to take action. On a batch plant the consequences may be different at each stage of the batch. On a continuous plant the consequences may be different during start-up, shut-down, catalyst regeneration, etc.

The Appendix to this Chapter (see Section A2.6 on page 43) describes a dangerous incident that occurred because the design and operating teams assumed that the computer would always take care of alarm situations and did not consider in detail the consequences of each action at each stage.

2.2 WHO CARRIES OUT A HAZOP?

A hazop is carried out by a team. For a new design the usual team is as follows:

PROJECT or DESIGN ENGINEER — Usually a mechanical engineer and, at this stage of the project, the person responsible for keeping the costs within the sum sanctioned. He wants to minimise changes but at the same time wants to find out now rather than later if there are any unknown hazards or operating problems.
PROCESS ENGINEER — Usually the chemical engineer who drew up the flowsheet.
COMMISSIONING MANAGER — Usually a chemical engineer, he will have to start up and operate the plant and is therefore inclined to press for any changes that will make life easier.
INSTRUMENT DESIGN ENGINEER — As modern plants contain sophisticated control and trip systems and as hazops often result in the addition of yet more instrumentation to the plant.
RESEARCH CHEMIST — If new chemistry is involved.
INDEPENDENT CHAIRMAN — He is an expert in the hazop technique, not the plant. His job is to ensure that the team follows the procedure. He needs to be skilled in leading a team of people who are not responsible to him and should be the sort of person who pays meticulous attention to detail. He may also supply the safety department's view on the points discussed. If not, a representative from this department should be present.

If the plant has been designed by a contractor, the hazop team should contain people from both the contractor and client organisations, and certain functions may have to be duplicated.

On a computer-controlled plant, particularly a computer-controlled batch plant, the applications engineer should be a member of the hazop team which should also include at least one other person who understands the computer logic. If the team does not include such a person, a dialogue is impossible and the team cannot be sure that the applications engineer understands the process and has met the design requirements. Refer to the Appendix to this Chapter, Section A2.6, page 43.

While the team members have a common objective — a safe and operable plant — the constraints on them are different. The designers, especially the design engineer responsible for costs, want to keep the costs down. The commissioning manager wants an easy start-up. This conflict of interests ensures that the pros and cons of each proposal are thoroughly explored before an agreed decision is reached. However, if the design engineer has a much stronger personality than the other members, the team may stray too far towards economy. Other teams may err the other way. The chairman should try to correct any imbalance. To quote Sir John Harvey-Jones, 'In industry the optimal level of conflict is not zero'[20].

If the team cannot agree, the chairman should suggest that the point is considered outside the meeting. Sometimes a decision is postponed while expert advice is sought — for example, from a materials expert — or even while research is carried out. Sometimes a decision is postponed so that a quantitative estimate of the hazard can be made, using the methods described in Chapter 3. Sometimes a quick, quantitative estimate can be made during the meeting (see Section 2.9).

Normally people's views converge towards agreement. If the chairman senses that views are getting further apart and that members of the team are starting to dig their heels in, he should suggest that the discussion on the point at issue is postponed and that someone prepares a note on the pros and cons of various possible courses of action, which can be circulated to all concerned.

If an existing plant is being studied then the team should include several people with experience of the existing plant. A typical team is:

PLANT MANAGER — Responsible for plant operation. (Note for US readers: in the UK the term, 'plant manager' describes someone who would be known as a supervisor or superintendent in most US companies.)
PROCESS FOREMAN — He knows what actually happens rather than what is supposed to happen.
PLANT ENGINEER — Responsible for mechanical maintenance, he knows many of the faults that occur.
INSTRUMENT MANAGER — Responsible for instrument maintenance including testing of alarms and trips, as well as the installation of new instruments.
PROCESS INVESTIGATION MANAGER — Responsible for investigating technical problems and for transferring laboratory results to plant scale operations.
INDEPENDENT CHAIRMAN

If an existing plant is being modified or extended, the team should consist of a combination of those described but do not let the team get too big as it holds up progress. Six or seven people are usually enough.

Hazop teams, apart from the chairman, do not require much training. They can pick up the techniques as they go along. If anyone is present for the first time, the chairman should start with 10 minutes of explanation. However, if possible, new team members should attend a half-day lecture and discussion based on this chapter. The Institution of Chemical Engineers can supply a set of notes and slides[33].

It might be thought that membership of a hazop team is 'the proper toil of artless industry, a task that requires neither the light of learning, nor the activity of genius, but may be successfully performed without any higher quality than that of bearing burthens with dull patience and ... sluggish resolution', to quote Dr Johnson[21]. This is not the case. The best team members are creative and uninhibited people who can think of new and original ways for things to go wrong and are not too shy to suggest them. In a hazop, do not hesitate to suggest impossibly crazy deviations, causes, consequences or solutions as they may lead other people to think of similar but possible deviations, etc.

Another feature of good team members is a mental ragbag of bits and pieces of knowledge that they have built up over the years. Such people may be able to recall that a situation similar to that under discussion caused an incident elsewhere. They need not remember the details so long as they can alert the team to possibilities that should be considered and perhaps investigated further. For an example, turn to the Appendix to this Chapter, Section A2.7.

Note that the team, except for the chairman, are experts on the process. They will, by this stage, have been immersed in it for 1–2 years. Hazop is not a technique for bringing fresh minds to work on a problem. It is a technique for allowing those expert in the process to bring their knowledge and experience to bear systematically, so that problems are less likely to be missed.

The complexity of modern plants make it difficult or impossible to see what might go wrong unless we go through the design systematically. Few accidents occur because the design team lack knowledge; most errors in design occur because the design team fail to apply their knowledge. Hazop gives them an opportunity to go through the design line by line, deviation by deviation to see what they have missed.

The team should have the authority to agree most changes there and then. Progress is slow if every change has to be referred to someone who is not present. The team members should try to avoid sending deputies. They lack the knowledge of previous meetings and might not have the authority to approve changes; as a result progress is held up.

The chairman often acts as secretary as well as safety department representative. He writes up his notes after the meeting and circulates them before the next meeting. As already stated, it is not necessary to write them up in the degree of detail shown in Table 2.2. Figure 2.3 shows a suggested form for the first few actions agreed in Table 2.2. However, the tendency today is to write up the notes in more detail than in the past, in the style of Table 2.2 rather than that of Figure 2.3, so that the company can demonstrate, if necessary, that they have done everything reasonably possible to identify the hazards.

Some companies consider that all hazops should be written up in great detail. If the design is queried in the future, the hazop records can be consulted. There is some force in the argument but the extra work is considerable and, in practice, hazop reports are rarely, if ever, consulted once the plant is on line.

A few weeks after the hazop the chairman should call the team together, check on progress made and recirculate the report form (Figure 2.3) with the 'Follow-up' column completed.

2.3 WHEN IS A HAZOP CARRIED OUT AND HOW LONG DOES IT TAKE?

A hazop cannot be carried out before the line diagrams (or process and instrumentation diagrams as they are often called) are complete. It should be carried out as soon as possible thereafter.

If an existing plant is being studied the first step is to bring the line diagrams up to date or check that they are up-to-date. Carrying out a hazop on an incorrect line diagram is the most useless occupation in the world. It is as effective as setting out on a journey with a railway timetable ten years out of date.

A hazop takes 1.5–3 hours per main plant item (still, furnace, reactor, heater, etc). If the plant is similar to an existing one it will take 1.5 hours per item but if the process is new it may take 3 hours per item.

Meetings are usually restricted to 3 hours, 2 or 3 days per week, to give the team time to attend to their other duties and because the imagination tires after 3 hours at a stretch.

The hazop on a large project may take several months, even with 2 or 3 teams working in parallel on different sections of the plant. It is thus necessary to either:

(a) Hold up detailed design and construction until the hazop is complete, or

(b) Allow detailed design and construction to go ahead and risk having to modify the detailed design or even alter the plant when the results of the hazop are known.

Ideally, the design should be planned to allow time for (a) but if completion is urgent (b) may have to be accepted.

Section 2.7 suggests that a preliminary hazop is carried out on the flowsheet before detailed design starts. This will take much less time than the hazop of the line diagrams.

Study title:	OLEFIN DIMERISATION UNIT		**Project No .....**	
Prepared by:	Independent Chairman (IC)		**Sheet 1 of .....**	
Study team:	Design Engineer (DE) Process Engineer (PE) Commissioning Manager (CM) Instrument Design Engineer (IDE) Research Chemist (RC) Independent Chairman (IC)		**Line Diagram Nos .....** **Date .....**	
Study ref. no.	**Operating deviation**	**Action notes and queries**	**Action by**	**Follow-up review comments**
1	No flow	Ensure good communications with intermediate storage.	CM	
2		Install low level alarm on settling tank LIC.	IDE	
3		Install kick-back on J1 pumps.	DE	
4		Check design of J1 pump strainers.	DE	
5		Institute regular patrolling and inspection of transfer line.	CM	
6	More flow	Install high level alarm on LIC.	IDE	
7		Check sizing of relief valve opposite liquid overfilling.	PE	
8		Institute locking off procedure for LIC by-pass when not in use.	CM	
9		Extend J2 pump suction line to 12" above tank base.	DE	

Figure 2.3 Hazard and operability study action report.

2.4 SOME POINTS TO WATCH DURING HAZOP

2.4.1 DON'T GET CARRIED AWAY

It is possible for a team to get carried away by enthusiasm and install expensive equipment to guard against unlikely hazards. The team leader can counter this by asking how often the hazard will occur and how serious the consequences will be. Sometimes he may suggest a full hazard analysis, as described in Chapter 3, but more often he can bring a problem into perspective by just quoting a few figures or asking a team member to do so. How often have similar pumps leaked in the past? How often do flanged joints leak and how far do the leaks spread? How often do operators forget to close a valve when an alarm sounds? Section 2.9 describes a 5-minute hazan carried out during a hazop meeting. The most effective team leaders are trained in hazan as well as hazop.

2.4.2 DIFFERENT SORTS OF ACTIONS

The team consists mainly of engineers. They like hardware solutions, but sometimes a hardware solution is impossible or too expensive and we have to make a change in methods or improve the training of the operators — that is, we change the software. We cannot spend our way out of every problem. Table 2.2 gives examples of software solutions as well as hardware ones.

Contractors, in particular, should choose solutions appropriate to the sophistication and experience of their client. It is no use installing elaborate trips if the client has neither the skill nor the will to use them. Less sophisticated solutions should be sought.

The actions agreed should normally be changes (in equipment or procedures) to prevent deviations occurring (or to give protection against the consequences or to provide opportunities for recovery), not actions to deal with the results of the deviation (such as handling a leak or fighting a fire). I have known hazop teams merely decide what they would do if a leak occurred, not how they would prevent it. While we should consider how we deal with those leaks that occur despite our efforts, the main emphasis in a hazop should be on prevention.

2.4.3 MODIFICATIONS

Many people believe that hazop is unsuitable for small modifications because it is difficult to assemble a team every time we wish to install a new valve or sample point or raise the operating temperature. However, many accidents have occurred because modifications had unforeseen and unpleasant side-effects[3,4]. If proposals are not 'hazoped', therefore, they should still be thoroughly probed before they are authorised. A guide sheet for helping us to do this is shown in Table 2.3 (see pages 22–23).

All modifications should be 'hazoped' or considered in a similiar way:

- temporary modifications as well as permanent ones;
- start-up modifications as well as those on established plants;
- cheap modifications as well as expensive ones;
- modifications to procedures as well as modifications to equipment.

References 3 and 4 describe many modifications which went wrong.

2.4.4 'WE DON'T NEED A HAZOP. WE EMPLOY GOOD PEOPLE AND RELY ON THEIR KNOWLEDGE AND EXPERIENCE'

A hazop is no substitute for knowledge and experience. It is not a sausage machine which consumes line diagrams and produces lists of modifications. It merely harnesses the knowledge and experience of the team in a systematic and concerted way. Because designs are so complicated the team cannot apply their knowledge and experience without this crutch for their thinking. If the team lacks knowledge and experience the hazop will produce nothing worthwhile.

'Good people' sometimes work in isolation. Pegram writes, 'working independently, the solving of a problem by one discipline can become a problem of another' and 'low cost engineering solutions from one point of view may not necessarily end up as overall low cost'[22]. Hazop ensures that hazards and operating problems are considered systematically by people from different functions working together. Experience shows that start-up, shut-down and other abnormal conditions are often overlooked by functional groups working in isolation. For an example, look at the last incident in the Appendix to this Chapter (Section A2.10).

2.4.5 'DO IT FOR US'

Companies have been known to say to a design contractor, 'We are understaffed and you are the experts, so why don't you do the hazop for us?'[23].

The client should be involved as well as the contractor because the client will have to operate the plant. The hazop will give the client's staff an understanding of the reasons for various design features and help them write the operating instructions. Even if the client's staff know little to start with about the problems specific to the particular process, they will be able to apply general chemical engineering and scientific knowledge as well as commonsense knowledge (see Section 2.6). Writing in a different context, Pegram says, '... The only effective team is one that owns the problem. The team must therefore comprise the individuals who are responsible for implementing the results of the study, not an external group of experts'[22]. The actions agreed at a hazop include changes in procedures as well as changes to equipment (see Section 2.4.2) and while the contractor is responsible for the latter, the client is responsible for the former. (In addition, Section 2.11 contains a note on the less obvious benefits of hazop.)

TABLE 2.3

A procedure for safety assessment of modifications (from Reference 3). A possible extra question is, 'What is the worst thing that can go wrong?'

Plant	Title	Reg. No.

Underline those factors which have been changed by the proposal

Process conditions	**Engineering hardware and design**
temperature	line diagram
pressure	wiring diagram
flow	plant layout
level	design pressure
composition	design temperature
toxicity	materials of construction
flash point	loads on, or strength of:
reaction conditions	foundations, structures, vessels
	pipework/supports/bellows
Operating methods	temporary or permanent:
start-up	pipework/supports/bellows
routine operation	valves, slip-plates
shutdown	restriction plates, filters
preparation for maintenance	instrumentation and control
abnormal operation	systems
emergency operation	trips and alarms
layout and positioning of controls	static electricity
and instruments	lightning protection
	radioactivity
Engineering methods	rate of corrosion
trip and alarm testing	rate of erosion
maintenance procedures	isolation for maintenance
inspection	mechanical-electrical
portable equipment	fire protection of cables
	handrails
Safety equipment	ladders
fire fighting and detection systems	platforms
means of escape	walkways
safety equipment for personnel	tripping hazard
	access for:
Environmental conditions	operation, maintenance, vehicles,
liquid effluent	plant, fire fighting
solid effluent	underground/overhead:
gaseous effluent	services
noise	equipment

(Table 2.3 continued opposite)

Within the categories listed below, does the proposal:	**Yes or no**	**What problems are created affecting plant or personnel safety? Recommended action?**	Signed and date
Relief and blowdown (1) Introduce or alter any potential cause of over/under pressuring the system or part of it? (2) Introduce or alter any potential cause of higher or lower temperature in the system or part of it? (3) Introduce a risk of creating a vacuum in the system or part of it? (4) In any way affect equipment already installed for the purpose of preventing or minimising over or under pressure? **Area classification** (5) Introduce or alter the location of potential leaks of flammable material? (6) Alter the chemical composition or the physical properties of the process material? (7) Introduce new or alter existing electrical equipment? **Safety equipment** (8) Require the provision of additional safety equipment? (9) Affect existing safety equipment? **Operation and design** (10) Introduce new or alter existing hardware? (11) Require consideration of the relevant Codes of Practice and Specifications? (12) Affect the process or equipment upstream or downstream of the change? (13) Affect safe access for personnel and equipment, safe places of work and safe layout? (14) Require revision of equipment inspection frequencies? (15) Affect any existing trip or alarm system or require additional trip or alarm protection? (16) Affect the reaction stability or controllability of the process? (17) Affect existing operating or maintenance procedures or require new procedures? (18) Alter the composition of, or means of disposal of effluent? (19) Alter noise levels?			
Safety assessor . . . . Date . . . . Checked by . . . . Plant Manager	Checked by . . . . Engineer		

2.4.6 KNOCK-ON EFFECTS

When a change in design (or operating conditions) is made during a hazop, it may have effects elsewhere in the plant, including the sections already studied.

For example, during a hazop the team decided to connect an alternative cooling water supply to a heat exchanger. The original water supply was clean but the alternative was contaminated, and so the team had to change the grade of steel used for the heat exchanger and connecting lines. They also had to consider the effects of reverse flow in the original lines[24].

2.4.7 'LEAVE IT UNTIL THE HAZOP'

Design engineers have been known to say, when someone suggests a change in design, 'Don't bother me now. We'll be having a hazop later on. Let's talk about it then'.

This is the wrong approach. A hazop should be a final check on a basically sound design to make sure that no unforeseen effects have been overlooked. It should not replace the normal consultations and discussions that take place while a design is being developed. A hazop meeting is not the right place for redesigning the plant; there are too many people present and it distracts from the main purpose of the meeting which is the critical examination of the design on the table[9].

2.5 AN EXAMPLE OF A HAZOP

Table 2.2 gives the results of a hazop on the plant shown in Figure 2.2[5]. It shows the feed section of a proposed olefin dimerisation unit and details are as follows:

An alkene/alkane fraction containing small amounts of suspended water is continuously pumped from a bulk intermediate storage tank via a 1 km (half-mile) pipeline into a buffer/settling tank where residual water is settled out prior to passing via a feed/product heat exchanger and preheater to the reaction section. The water, which has an adverse effect on the dimerisation catalyst, is run off manually from the settling tank at intervals. Residence time in the reaction section must be held within closely defined limits to ensure adequate conversion of the alkene and to avoid excessive formation of polymer.

This design has proved valuable as a training exercise as it provides examples of many different aspects of hazop and may also introduce students to a number of chemical engineering points that they have not previously met, as shown by the following notes. The item numbers refer to the 'Possible causes' column of Table 2.2 and the letters to the 'Action required' column.

(1) Right at the start we see that the first two actions required are a software one and a hardware one, thus emphasising that hazop is not just concerned with the hardware. This first item brings the commissioning manager's attention to the

fact that his raw material comes from a storage area 1 km away controlled by a different manager and operators who do not have to cope with the results of a loss of feed. Whose job is it to monitor the stock and see that it does not run out? Although the storage operator is on the job, the plant operators have more incentive as they will have to deal with the consequences if the stock runs out.

Note that a deviation in one line may produce consequences elsewhere in the plant. Thus no flow in the line we are studying in this example may have effects further on in the plant, in the line leading to the reactor, where no flow may result in higher temperatures and the formation of polymer. In a batch process a deviation at one stage may have consequences at a later stage (see Appendix, Section A2.9).

(1)(b) A low flow alarm might be installed instead of a low level alarm but it is better to measure directly what we want to know, and the low level alarm is cheaper.

(3)(c) Note that a kick-back line is shown after pump J2 on the next line to be studied. A kick-back is cheaper than a high-temperature trip and requires less maintenance. Students should be reminded that the lifetime cost of an instrument is about twice the capital cost (after discounting) if testing and maintenance are included. Instruments (and computers) cost twice what you think they will cost.

(4) Line fracture is unlikely but serious. How far should we go in taking precautions? This item can produce a lively debate between those who wish to ignore the problem and those who want leak detectors, emergency isolation valves, etc. The action agreed is a compromise.

(5)(f) This illustrates the need, in sizing relief valves, to ask whether they have to pass gas or liquid.

(5)(g) Locking-off the by-pass makes it harder to open it quickly if the control valve fails shut. Do we need a by-pass? How often will the control valve fail shut?

(5)(h) The team might have decided that they wished to increase the size of the buffer/settling tank, originally sufficient for 20 minutes settling time but reduced by the action proposed. If so, they might have found that it was too late to do so as the vessel was on the critical path and had already been ordered. Section 2.7 recommends a preliminary hazop on the flowsheet at a time when such changes *can* be made.

(6) This item introduces students to liquid hammer which they may not have met before.

Note that we often have more than one chance to pick up a hazard. When discussing 'no flow' [item (3)] the team realised that line blockage would cause a rise in pressure but they decided to leave discussion of the consequences until they came to the deviation 'more pressure'. If they had not realised, when discussing item (3), that line blockage could cause a rise in pressure, then they had another opportunity to do so later. Sections 2.8.4 and A2.8 describe other examples.

(9) Some drains in Figure 2.2 are shown blanked, others not. All drains should be blanked unless used regularly by the process team.

(11) Regular draining of the intermediate storage tank will prevent gross amounts of water going forward to the settling tank. Can we not rely on the storage operator? Is a high interface alarm necessary? On the other hand excess water will damage the catalyst. It is unwise to rely for its removal on a man in another plant who may not realise its importance and does not suffer if the water goes forward.

An automatic controller to remove water, operated by the interface level indicator, is not recommended as if it fails oil will flow to drain and may not be detected.

(12) Have the distillation columns been designed for a particular concentration of lower alkanes and alkenes (and a particular alkane/alkene ratio) or a range of concentrations? If the former, what will be the effect of changes in concentration and ratio on throughput and performance? This item brings home to students that in designing equipment they should always ask what departure from flowsheet can be expected and estimate the effects on their design.

Reference 5 gives the results of a hazop of a second line in the dimerisation unit. Other examples of hazops can be found in References 6, 7, 8, 13 and 14. The examples described in References 7 and 8 are rather complex for a first exercise but those described in References 6, 13 and 14 should be suitable. Reference 6 deals with a plant in which a gas stream is heated and then passes to a compressor suction catchpot which is fitted with a high level alarm and a high level trip. Reference 13 studies a system for heating refrigerated propane before pumping it down a long mild steel pipeline to a receiving plant. The reliability of the heating system must be high or the pipeline may get too cold and become brittle. Reference 14 studies a nitric acid plant.

Reference 7 describes a study on a complex, highly-instrumented system for preventing reverse flow while Reference 8, part of the Institution of Chemical Engineer's model design project, describes a system of several reactors fitted with remotely-operated changeover valves.

Roach and Lees[9] have analysed the activities that take place during a hazop.

2.6 COULD A COMPUTER CARRY OUT A HAZOP?

Computers can certainly be used as an aid in hazop studies. Several programs are available for recording the results of studies, and the programs can also remind teams of the possible causes of various deviations and possible remedies so that they are less likely to overlook them. Thus if the team is considering 'no flow' in a pipeline, the computer can remind them that possible causes are an empty suction vessel, a pump failure (which in turn could be due to failure of the power supply, the motor, the coupling or the pump itself), a blockage, a closed valve, a slip-plate, a broken pipe or high pressure in the delivery vessel. Turney[32] has reviewed the features needed in these systems. However, these are not what people mean when they ask the question about computers and a hazop. They are asking if the computer could examine the line diagram, say what deviations can occur, and why, and suggest changes to the design or method of operation, perhaps using an expert system. And the answer, I think, is NO or, at least, not within the forseeable future, for two reasons.

The first reason is that hazop is a creative exercise and those who are best at it are people who can let their minds go free and think of all the possible ways in which deviations might occur and possible methods of prevention and control (see Section 2.2). To quote from a book on artificial intelligence, '... these sort of techniques ... may eventually produce machines with a capacity for manipulating logical rules that will match, or even exceed, our own. But logic is just one aspect of human intelligence, and one whose importance can easily be overrated. For ... factors such as intuition and flair pay a very large part in our thinking, even in areas like science where logic ostensibly reigns supreme. For example, most of the scientists who have recounted how they came to make an important discovery or to achieve a significant breakthrough have stressed that when they found the answer to the crucial problem they intuitively recognised it to be right and only subsequently went back and worked out why it was right'[25].

The second reason is that the knowledge used in a hazop is 'broad and deep' while expert systems are suitable only for 'narrow and deep' knowledge[26].

The knowledge used in a hazop can be divided into four types[26] (see Figure 2.4 on page 28). The following examples of each type are taken from the hazop of the dimerisation plant described in Section 2.5:

PLANT SPECIFIC KNOWLEDGE

For example, the monomer may polymerise if it is kept too long at reaction temperature. It should be possible to put this knowledge into an expert system but it would not be worth the effort as the information would be useful only for one study (and perhaps for later studies of plant extensions or modifications).

GENERAL PROCESS ENGINEERING KNOWLEDGE

For example, a pump pumping against a dead head will overheat and this may lead to gland failure, a leak and a fire; if the residence time in a settler falls,

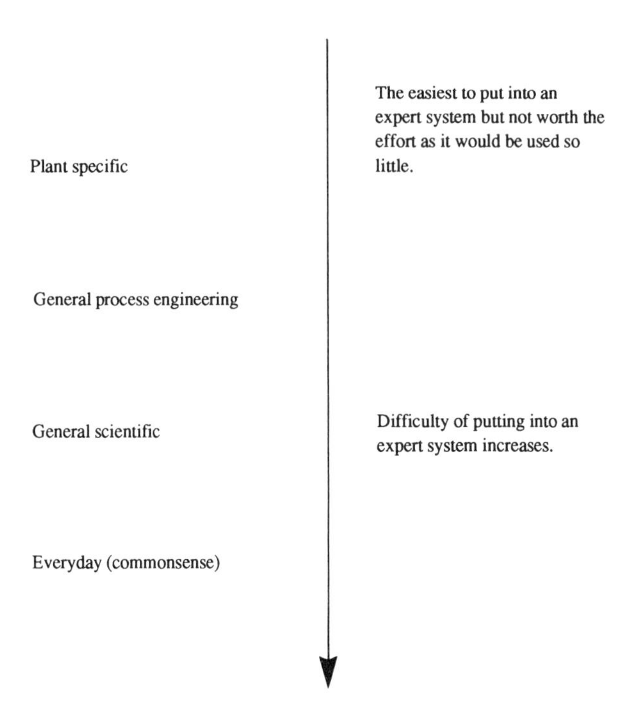

Figure 2.4 Types of knowledge.

settling may be incomplete. It should be possible in theory to put this knowledge into an expert system but the task would be enormous — a vast amount of knowledge would have to be incorporated, much of it 'good engineering practice' which is not usually written down. Expert systems are most suitable for restricted subject areas (knowledge domains). Furthermore, engineers 'know what they don't know' — know (or should know) the limitations of their knowledge and when they ought to call in an expert. It would be difficult to incorporate this 'negative knowledge' into an expert system. An expert system could be used during hazop to answer questions on, say, corrosion to avoid calling in a corrosion expert, but only the team can tell that they are getting out of their depth and that it is time to call in the expert (human or otherwise).

GENERAL SCIENTIFIC KNOWLEDGE

For example, water may freeze if the temperature falls below 0°C; if a closed system full of liquid is heated, the pressure will rise. The difficulty of putting the knowledge into an expert system is even greater than in Case 2.

EVERYDAY OR COMMONSENSE KNOWLEDGE

For example, if a line is broken, the contents will leak out; the men who have to cope with the effects of plant upsets are more likely than other men to take action to prevent them; a man cannot hear the telephone if he is out of earshot. The difficulties here are greater still and probably beyond the power of any expert system in the foreseeable future. To quote from Reference 24 again, 'The knowledge employed by an expert, unlike the commonplace, casually acquired knowledge we rely on in our everyday affairs, is likely to be formalized, codifiable and, above all, already fitted into a deductive framework. The reasoning processes employed by a doctor making a diagnosis, an engineer analysing a design or a lawyer preparing a brief are, in other words, much more nearly analogous to a computer running a program than the vague and ill-defined sort of reasoning we engage in when we think about more mundane matters'. In hazop we are concerned with mundane matters as well as purely technical ones, as Section 2.5 shows.

So, hazop teams are unlikely to become redundant in the forseeable future.

2.7 THE LIMITATIONS OF HAZOP (see also Appendix, Section A2.10)

Hazop as described above is carried out late in design. It brings hazards and operating problems to light at a time when they can be put right with an india-rubber rather than a welding set, but at a time when it is too late to make fundamental changes in design.

For example, referring to Section 2.5, note (12), the hazop might bring to light the fact that the concentration of light ends might vary markedly from design and that the still should be redesigned to allow for this. It is probably too late to do this; the still may have already been ordered. Section 2.5, note (5)(h), contains another example.

Such problems can be picked up earlier if a preliminary or 'coarse-scale' hazop is carried out on the flowsheet before it is passed to the engineering department for detailed design, a year or more before the line diagrams are available. Like a normal hazop it can be applied to continuous and batch plants.

The following are some of the points brought out in a preliminary hazop of the design for a batch reactor, followed by a stripping section in which an excess of one reactant is removed under vacuum.

- If the reactor is overfilled it overflows into a pot which is fitted with a high level alarm. Why not fit the high level alarm on the reactor and dispense with the pot?
- What would it cost to design the reactor to withstand the vacuum produced

by the stripper, thus avoiding the need for a vacuum relief valve which would allow air to be sucked into the reactor, producing a flammable mixture?

- Why do we need two filters per reactor? Will a change in type allow us to manage with one?
- By suitable choice of bottoms pump, can we reduce the height of the stripper above ground level and thus reduce the cost of the structure?
- Can the heat exchangers be designed to withstand the maximum pressures that can be developed under all but fire conditions, thus avoiding the need for relief valves?
- A material proposed for removal of colour may be unsuitable on toxicological grounds.

These are just a few of the 66 points that came up during three 3-hour meetings. Many of the points would have come up in any case but without a hazop many might have been missed or might not have come up until it was too late to change the design.

While the results of several line diagram hazops have been described in detail (see the list at end of Section 2.5), very few flowsheet hazops have been described in the same way. However, Reference 15 describes many changes that have been made as a result of flowsheet hazops and References 11 and 12 describe two early studies of flowsheets using critical examination (see Section 7.1) rather than hazop.

An important difference between an ordinary hazop and a coarse-scale hazop of a flowsheet should be noted. In an ordinary hazop deviations from design are considered undesirable. We look for causes of deviations and ways of preventing them. In coarse-scale hazop, however, we are also trying to generate alternatives. In considering, say, 'more of' temperature, we do not just ask if it can occur and if it would be undesirable but we also ask if it might not be better to operate at higher temperatures.

Hazop — designed to generate deviations — was developed from a technique — critical examination — which was designed to generate alternatives. To generate alternatives we may therefore need to go back to something akin to the original technique. In particular, we may need an extra guide word, AVOID (the need). Table 2.4 (from Reference 11) is an extract from an early critical examination of a flowsheet.

Even a coarse-scale hazop is too late for some major changes in plant design. A similar type of study is needed at the conceptual or business analysis stage when we decide which product to make, by what route and where to locate the plant. For example, at Bhopal in 1984 an intermediate, methyl isocyanate (MIC), leaked out of a large continuous plant and killed over 2000 people. If the

TABLE 2.4
An extract from the critical examination of a flowsheet showing the generation of alternatives by successive questioning (from Reference 11)

Statement: Design a distillation column

Successive questions	Alternative ideas generated
Why? To separate A from B.	(i) Separate them some other way, eg fractional crystallisation. (ii) Don't separate them at all.
Why? Because the recycle reactor won't crack A mixed with B.	(i) Find an alternative market which will take A and B. (ii) Change the process so we don't make B.
Why? Because the furnace temperature isn't high enough.	(i) Change the reactor conditions so that A and B can be cracked.
Why? Because tube materials won't stand a higher temperature.	(i) Find another tube material to stand higher temperatures. (ii) Find catalyst to permit cracking at lower temperature.

same raw materials are allowed to react in a different order, no MIC is produced. It is too late to suggest at the flowsheet stage that the order of reaction, on a continuous plant, should be changed. That decision has to be made right at the beginning of the design process (see also Appendix, Section A2.2).

Alternatively, if we use the MIC route we can reduce or eliminate the intermediate stock and use the MIC as soon as it is formed. The decision to do so can be made at any time, even when the plant is on line, but money will be saved if the decision is made early in design.

A theologian[27] once said, ' ... all great controversies depend on both sides sharing a false premise'. In controversies about whether or not to spend money on a particular safety proposal, the design engineer may think he has gone far enough and the commissioning manager may disagree. The common false premise is the belief that we have to spend money to increase safety. If safety studies are made early in design this is not the case; plants can be both cheaper and safer[15].

A clever man has been described as one who finds ways out of an unpleasant situation into which a wise man would never have got himself. Wise men carry out safety studies early in design.

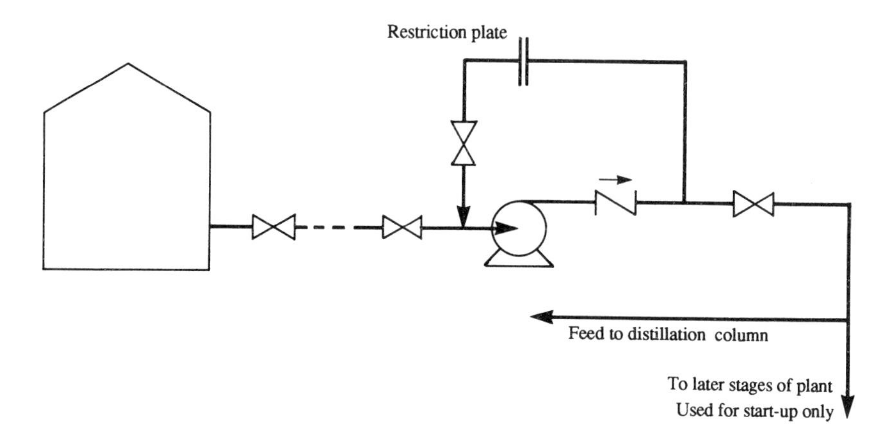

Figure 2.5 Twelve points came out of a hazop in this bit of plant.

Of course, every company carries out many studies before embarking on a design. What is lacking, however, in most companies at the conceptual and flowsheet stages of projects, is the systematic, formal, structured examination which is characteristic of a hazop. The normal hazop questions are not suitable at the conceptual stage but Chapter 10 of Reference 15 suggests some alternatives. It also gives many examples of hazards that have been or could be reduced or avoided by hazop type studies at the conceptual or flowsheet stages.

A nuisance during a conventional hazop is the man who asks if the right product is being made in the right way at the right place. It is by then far too late to ask such questions. If he asks them then, perhaps he had no opportunity to ask them earlier.

2.8 'DO WE NEED TO HAZOP THIS PLANT?' 'IT IS ONLY A SIMPLE PROJECT' OR 'IT IS SIMILAR TO THE LAST ONE'

2.8.1 AN EXAMPLE

So many of the things that go wrong occur on small, simple or repeat units where people feel that the full treatment is unnecessary. 'It is only a storage project and we have done many of these before!' 'It is only a pipeline and a couple of pumps.' 'It is only a service system.'

If designers talk like this, suggest they try a hazop and see what comes out of it. After the first meeting or two they usually want to continue.

Figure 2.5 shows part of a line diagram on which the design team were persuaded, somewhat reluctantly, to carry out a hazop. Twelve points which had been overlooked came out of the study. Here are four of them:

- If the pump stops, reverse flow will occur through the kick-back line. The non-return valve should be downstream of this line.
- If the pump stops, reverse flow may occur through the start-up line. Should there be a non-return valve in this line?
- The restriction plate in the kick-back line might be replaced by a flow controller to save power.
- No provision has been made for slip-rings or spectacle plates so that the pump can be isolated by slip-plates for maintenance.

The design team readily agreed to study the rest of the plant.

2.8.2 ANOTHER EXAMPLE

The tank shown in Figure 2.6 was being filled from another tank some distance away. The pump used for emptying the tank was not running but its kick-back line had been left open. When the tank was nearly full the high level trip closed the valve in the filling line. The gauge pressure in the filling line rose to 20 bar (300 psi) and burst the pump which normally operated at a gauge pressure of 3 bar (45 psi).

A hazop had been carried out on the plant, but this section was not studied as it was 'only an off-plot', a tank, a pump and a few valves — too simple for any hazards to pass unnoticed, or so it was thought. Consideration of 'reverse flow' through the kick-back line (or 'more of pressure' in the filling line) would have disclosed the hazard.

After the incident the kick-back line was rerouted back to the tank.

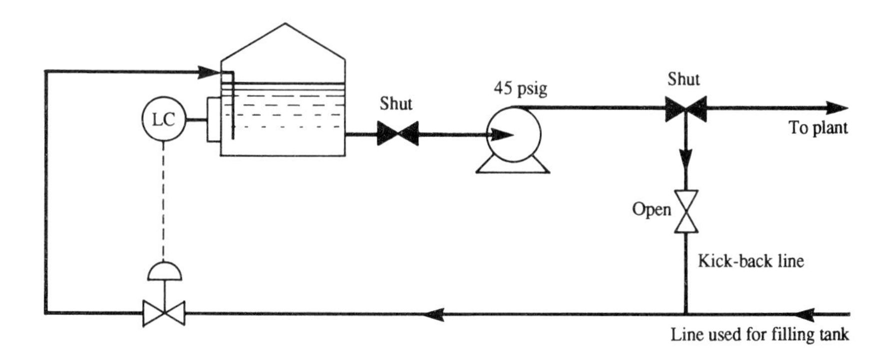

Figure 2.6 When the automatic valve closed, the pump was overpressured.

2.8.3 SERVICE SYSTEMS

All service lines (including steam, water, compressed air, nitrogen and drain lines) should be 'hazoped' as well as process lines (see Appendix, Section A2.3 and A2.5). Pearson[16] lists some of the questions which arise during hazops of service systems:

- Should power supplies to equipment be duplicated?
- Should equipment be duplicated or triplicated?
- Should we use steam or electricity or a combination for pumps and compressors?
- Should we provide automatic start for spare pumps?
- Should we provide voltage protection for key equipment which must be kept on line or restarted quickly?
- In which order should equipment be restarted after a power failure?
- Do we need emergency power supplies for lighting, communication equipment, etc?
- Should control valves fail open or shut or 'stay put'?
- How will emergency equipment such as diesel generators be cooled if plant cooling water is not available?

2.8.4 SMALL BRANCHES

Do not overlook small branches which may not have been given a line number. For example, a tank was fitted with a tundish so that it could be dosed with stabilising chemicals. The effects of adding too much or too little additive (or the wrong additive, or adding it at the wrong time) should obviously be considered during hazop but might be overlooked if the team studied only lines with line numbers. (On the other hand they might have picked it up by considering operations taking place inside a vessel, as suggested in Section 2.1; another example of the way in which hazop often gives us a second chance[24].)

2.9 THE USE OF QUANTITATIVE METHODS DURING HAZOP

The following example shows how a quick calculation can resolve a difference of opinion between the members of a hazop team. It acts as a link to the next Chapter in which numerical methods are considered in more detail.

On a design a compressor suction catchpot was fitted with a level controller and a high level trip to shut down the machine (Figure 2.7). The commissioning manager asked for a second independent trip as failure of the trip could result in damage to the machine which would be expensive to repair. The design engineer, responsible for controlling the cost, was opposed: this, he

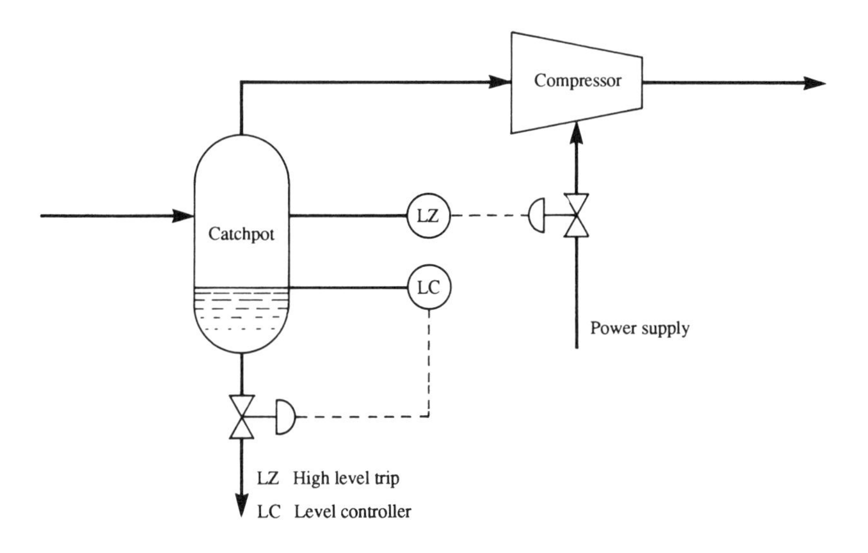

Figure 2.7 Do we need a second high level trip?

said, would be gold-plating. A simple calculation (see Section 3.5 for an explanation of the terms used) helped to resolve the conflict.

The trip will have a fail-danger rate of once in two years. With monthly testing the fractional dead time will be 0.02.

The demand rate results from the failure of the level controller. Experience shows that a typical figure is once every two years or 0.5/year. A hazard will therefore occur once in 100 years or, more precisely, there is a 1 in 100 chance that it will occur in any one year or in a 1 in 10 chance that it will occur during the 10-year life of the plant. Everyone agreed that this was too high.

They also saw that there was more than one way of reducing the hazard rate. They could improve the control system and reduce the demand rate, or they could improve the trip system and reduce the fractional dead time. It may not be necessary to duplicate all the trip system; it may be sufficient to duplicate the trip initiator.

2.10 THE USE OF HAZOP IN OTHER INDUSTRIES

Hazop was pioneered in the chemical industry (see Chapter 7) and soon spread to the oil industry and later to food processing, both basically similar industries. In the food industry the emphasis has been on identifying ways in which contamination could occur rather than other operating and safety problems. This section discusses some other applications.

In considering whether or not hazop could be applied in a new context, remember that hazop grew out of critical examination (see Section 7.1) and that the original form of the technique may be more suitable than the modification (hazop) developed to meet the process industry's needs.

Hazop has been applied to laboratory design[10] and to laboratory operations. One study of a new operation disclosed the fact that the chemists intended to convey cylinders of hydrogen cyanide to the top floor in the lift!

Hazop has also been applied to the manufacture of a product using genetically modified organisms (GMOs)[28]. A modification of hazop known as GENHAZ has been proposed for identifying ways in which GMOs might affect the environment[29].

2.10.1 MECHANICAL HAZARDS

Knowlton[2] has described the application of hazop to some mechanical problems. For example, a sterilisation autoclave had to be loaded with a stack of trays using a fork lift truck. Application of the deviation 'more of' disclosed that if the driver moved the load too far forward it could damage the rear wall of the autoclave. Application of the deviation 'as well as' disclosed that if the driver raised the load it could damage an instrument that measured the humidity and perhaps also damage the roof.

Similarly, too rapid operation could cause spillage and led the team to ask how spillages would be handled.

2.10.2 NUCLEAR POWER

The nuclear power industry was slow to adopt hazop, preferring instead a technique known as failure mode and effect analysis (FMEA).

In hazop we start with a deviation and ask how it might occur. For example, 'more of flow' in a pipeline might be caused by the failure of a flow controller. There will probably be other possible causes as well (see Table 2.2). In FMEA we start with a component and work out the consequences of failure. If we start with the flow controller, one of the consequences of its failure may be too high a flow in a pipeline. There will probably be other consequences as well.

In the line diagram sense, the essentials of a nuclear reactor are relatively simple: a hot core heats water. In this sense it is much simpler than the average chemical plant. On the other hand, the nuclear reactor contains far more protective equipment to prevent it getting out of control and to commission emergency cooling systems, etc. The obvious first approach of the nuclear engineers was therefore to ask, 'What will happen if a component of the protective systems fails?' and then examine each component in turn.

However, the cooling systems (normal and stand-by) and service lines on nuclear power stations would benefit from hazop and this is now recognised.

2.11 CONCLUSION

Carling[30] has described the effects of using hazop in his company. The benefits went far beyond a simple list of recommendations for a safer plant. The interaction between team members brought about a profound change in individual and departmental attitudes. Staff began to seek one another out to discuss possible consequences of proposed changes, problems were discussed more openly, departmental rivalries and barriers receded. The dangers of working in isolation and the consequences of ill-judged and hasty actions became better appreciated. Knowledge, ideas and experience became shared more fully to the benefit of the individual and the company.

Carling's company adopted hazop after experiencing several serious incidents. Buzzelli writes[31], 'For an industry so proud of its technical safety achievement it is humbling to have to admit that most of our significant safety improvements were developed in response to plant accidents'.

It does not have to be so. Hazop provides us with a lantern on the bow (Chapter 1), a way of of seeing hazards before they wreck our plant.

REFERENCES IN CHAPTER 2

1. Chemical Industries Association, London, 1977, *Hazard and operability studies*.
2. Knowlton, R.E., 1981, *An introduction to hazard and operability studies*, Chemetics International, Vancouver, Canada.
3. Kletz, T.A., November 1976, *Chemical Engineering Progress*, 72 (11): 48.
4. Kletz, T.A., 1988, *What went wrong?—Case histories of process plant disasters*, 2nd edition, Gulf Publishing Co., Houston, Texas, Chapter 2, and *Lees*, Chapter 21.
5. Lawley, H.G., April 1974, *Chemical Engineering Progress*, 70 (4): 45.
6. Rushford, R., 21 March 1977, *North-East Coast Institution of Engineers and Shipbuilders: Transactions*, 93: 117.
7. Lawley, H.G., April 1976, *Hydrocarbon Processing*, 55 (4): 247. Reprinted in *Fire protection manual for hydrocarbon processing plants*, Vol. 2, 1981, edited by C.H. Vervalin, Gulf Publishing Co., Houston, Texas, 1981, 94.
8. Austin, D.G. and Jeffreys, G.V., 1979, *The manufacture of methyl ethyl ketone from 2-butanol*, Institution of Chemical Engineers, Rugby, UK, Chapter 12.
9. Roach, J. and Lees, F.P., October 1981, *The Chemical Engineer*, No. 373, 456.
10. Knowlton, R.E, 1976, *R & D Management*, 7 (1): 1.
11. Elliott, D.M. and Owen, J.M., 1968, *The Chemical Engineer*, No. 223, CE 377.
12. Binstead, D.S., 16 January 1960, *Chemistry and Industry*, 59.
13. Kletz, T.A., 1 April 1985, *Chemical Engineering*, 92 (7): 48.
14. Sinnott, R.K., 1983, in *Chemical engineering*, edited by J.M. Coulson and J.F. Richardson, Vol. 6, Pergamon Press, Oxford, Chapter 9.5.

15. Kletz, T.A., 1991, *Plant design for safety —a user-friendly approach*, Hemisphere, New York.
16. Pearson, L., 1984, The operation of utility systems, *Institution of Chemical Engineers Loss Prevention Subject Group Meeting, 11 September 1984*.
17. Ozog, H., 18 February 1985, *Chemical Engineering*, 161.
18. Kletz, T.A., 1988, *Learning from accidents in industry*, Butterworths, Chapter 9.
19. Health and Safety Executive, March 1977, *The explosion at the Dow chemical factory, King's Lynn, 27 June 1976*, HMSO, London.
20. Harvey-Jones, J.H., 1988, *Making it happen*, Collins, London, 28.
21. Johnson, S., 1755, *A dictionary of the English language*, Introduction.
22. Pegram, N., 27 September 1990, *The Chemical Engineer*, No. 482, 37.
23. McKelvey, T.C. and Zerafa, M.J., 1990, Vital hazop leadership skills and techniques, *American Institute of Chemical Engineers Summer National Meeting, San Diego, California, 19–22 August 1990.*
24. Rushton, A.G., 1989, Computer integrated process engineering, *Symposium Series No. 114*, Institution of Chemical Engineers, 27.
25. Aleksander, I. and Burnett, P., 1987, *Thinking machines*, Knopf, New York, 107, 196.
26. Ferguson, G. and Andow, P.K., 1986, Process plant safety and artificial intelligence, *World Congress of Chemical Engineering, Tokyo, 1986*, Paper 14-153, Vol. II, 1092.
27. A 4th century theologian quoted by N. MacGregor, February 1991, *Royal Society of Arts Journal*, 139 (5415): 191.
28. Gustafson, R.M., Stahr, J.J. and Burke, D.H., 1987, The use of safety and risk assessment procedures in the analysis of biological process systems: a case study of the Verax System 2000, *ASME 105th Winter Annual Meeting, 13-18 December 1987.*
29. Royal Commission on Environmental Pollution, 1991, *Fourteenth report: a system for the critical appraisal of proposals to release genetically modified organisms into the environment*, HMSO, London.
30. Carling, N., 1987, Hazop study of BAPCO's FCCU complex, *American Petroleum Institute Committee on Safety and Fire Protection Spring Meeting, Denver, Colorado, 8–11 April 1986.*
31. Buzzelli, D.T., July 1990, *Plant/Operations Progress*, 9 (3): 145.
32. Turney, R.D., 1991, The application of Total Quality Management to hazard studies and their recording, *Symposium Series No. 124*, Institution of Chemical Engineers, Rugby, UK, 299.
33. Anon, 1990, *Slide training package in Hazop and Hazan*, Institution of Chemical Engineers, Rugby, UK.

APPENDIX TO CHAPTER 2 — SOME ACCIDENTS THAT COULD HAVE BEEN PREVENTED BY HAZARD AND OPERABILITY STUDIES

A2.1 REVERSE FLOW

Many accidents have occurred because process materials flowed in the opposite direction to that expected and the fact that this could occur was not foreseen. For example, ethylene oxide and ammonia were allowed to react to make ethanolamine. Some ammonia flowed from the reactor, in the wrong direction, along the ethylene oxide transfer line into the ethylene oxide tank, past several non-return valves and a positive pump. It got past the pump through the relief valve which discharged into the pump suction line. The ammonia reacted with 30 m^3 of ethylene oxide in the tank which ruptured violently. The released ethylene oxide vapour exploded causing damage and destruction over a wide area[1].

A hazard and operability study would have disclosed the fact that reverse flow could occur. Reference 7 of Chapter 2 describes in detail a hazop of a similar installation.

On another occasion some paraffin passed from a reactor up a chlorine transfer line and reacted with liquid chlorine in a catchpot. Bits of the catchpot were found 30 m away[2].

On many occasions process materials have entered service lines, either because the service pressure was lower than usual or the process pressure was higher than usual. The contamination has then spread via the service lines (steam, air, nitrogen, water) to other parts of the plant. On one occasion ethylene entered a steam main through a leaking heat exchanger. Another branch of the steam main supplied a space heater in the basement of the control room and the condensate was discharged to an open drain inside the building. Ethylene accumulated in the basement, and was ignited (probably by the electric equipment, which was not protected), destroying the building. Again, a hazard and operability study would have disclosed the route taken by the ethylene.

For other examples of accidents that could be prevented by hazop, see Reference 3.

A2.2 BHOPAL

On 3 December 1984 there was a leak of methyl isocyanate from a storage tank in the Union Carbide plant at Bhopal, India and the vapour spread beyond the plant boundary to a shanty town which had grown up around the plant. Over 2000 people were killed. According to the official company report[4] the material in the tank had become contaminated with water and chloroform, causing a runaway reaction. The precise route of the contamination is not known, it may have been due to sabotage[8], but a hazop might have shown up possible ways in which contamination could have occurred and would have drawn attention to the need to keep all supplies of water well away from methyl isocyanate, with which it reacts violently.

However, there was much more wrong at Bhopal than the lack of a hazop. When the relief valve on the storage tank lifted, the scrubbing system which should have absorbed the vapour, the flare system which should have burned any vapour which got past the scrubbing system and the refrigeration system which should have kept the tank cool were out of commission or not in full working order. As stated in Chapter 1, hazop is a waste of time if the assumptions on which it is based — that the plant will be operated in the manner assumed by the designer and in accordance with good practice — are not true.

Equally important, was it really necessary to store so much hazardous material? Methyl isocyanate was an intermediate, not a product or raw material, convenient but not essential to store. A hazop on the flowsheet or a similar study at the earlier conceptual stage, as suggested in Section 2.7, might have led the decision team to question the need for so much intermediate storage. 'What you don't have, can't leak'[5].

A2.3 A FIRE IN A WATER SUMP

The sump shown in Figure 2.8 contained water with a layer of light oil on top. Welding had to take place nearby so the sump was emptied completely with an ejector and filled with clean water to the level of the overflow pipe. When a spark fell into the sump, there was an explosion and fire. The U-bend had not been emptied and there was a layer of oil in the bend on top of the water.

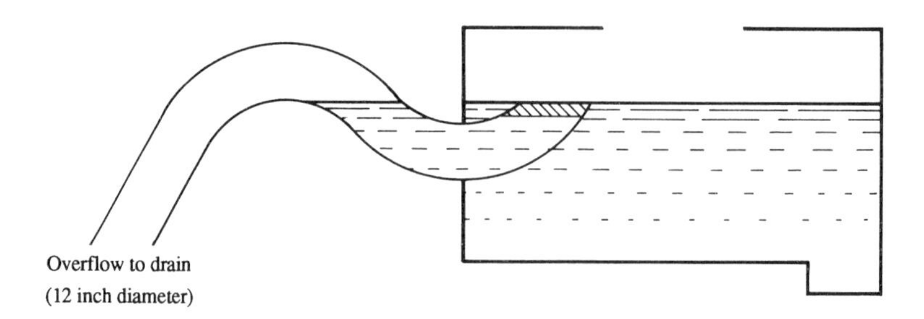

Figure 2.8 The sump was emptied and filled with clean water but oil was left in the U-bend.

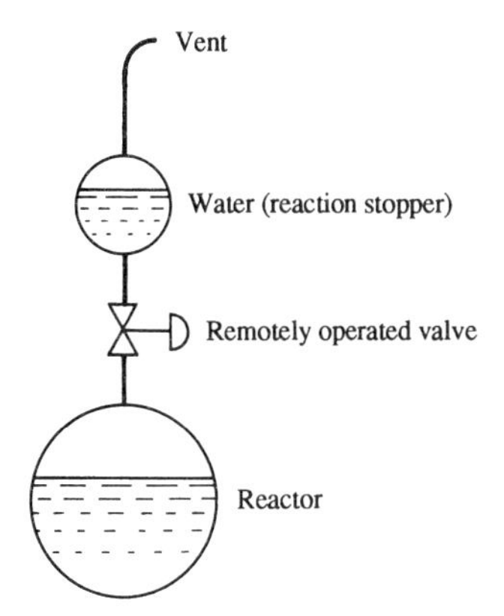

Figure 2.9 When a runaway reaction occurred, instead of the water entering the reactor, the increased pressure blew out the water.

A hazop would have disclosed the hazard if the preparation of the equipment for maintenance had been considered. The equipment got little consideration during design as it was not part of the main plant, only a system for collecting a waste water stream. See Section 2.8.

A2.4 A PROTECTIVE DEVICE THAT DID NOT WORK

A reactor was fitted with a head tank containing water (Figure 2.9). If the contents of the reactor got too hot and the reaction started to run away, the operator was supposed to open the remotely operated valve so that the water would flow by gravity into the reactor and cool the contents. Unfortunately the designers overlooked the fact that when the reaction started to run away the pressure in the reactor would rise. When the valve was opened the water was blown out of the vent! The reactor exploded and the subsequent fire destroyed the unit[9].

A2.5 SERVICES AND MODIFICATIONS: TWO NEGLECTED AREAS

A blown fuse de-energised part of an instrument panel and the trip system shut the plant down safely: a turbine and pumps stopped, flows stopped and the furnace tripped. The condensate pumps continued to run, as planned, so that the steam drum which fed the waste heat boilers did not get empty. In fact it filled

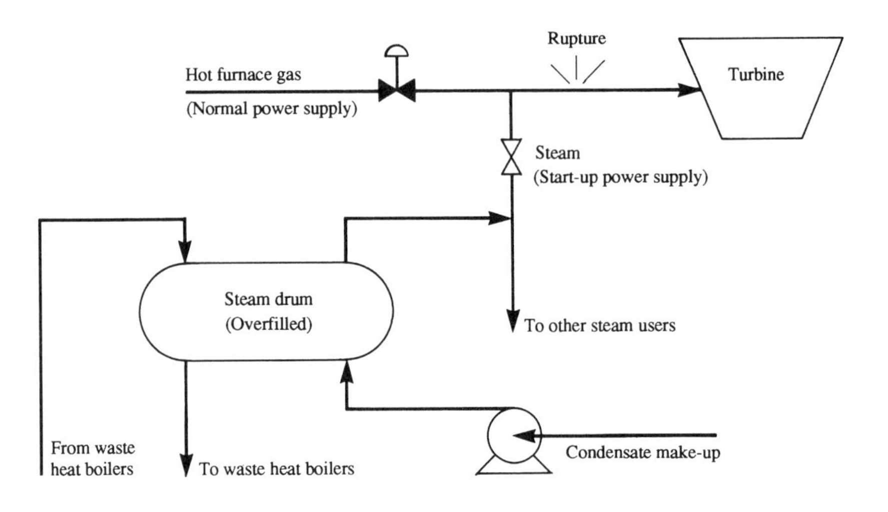

Figure 2.10 When the steam valve was opened condensate entered the hot line from the furnace.

up completely in two minutes and the condensate overflowed into the steam main (Figure 2.10).

The turbine was driven by hot gases from the furnace but could be started with steam. The operators decided to turn the turbine slowly (to prevent damage to the shaft). As no furnace gas was available they cracked open the steam valve. Condensate came into contact with the hot line from the furnace and the line ruptured. Three men were sprayed with steam and hot condensate and two of them were killed.

Hazops should consider the results of power and other service failures (see Section 2.8) and the action to be taken should be covered in plant training and instructions.

The plant instrumentation had originally been very well organised but, as instruments were removed and others added, it became difficult to tell which instruments were connected to which power supply. All modifications, including modifications to instrument and electrical systems, should be reviewed by hazop or, if they are minor, by a similar technique (see Section 2.4.3).

After the incident the steam drum was made larger so that it contained enough condensate to remove residual heat from the process without make-up, an inherently safer design[10].

A2.6 A COMPUTER-CONTROLLED BATCH REACTION (Figure 2.11)

The computer was programmed so that, if a fault occurred in the plant, all controlled variables would be left as they were and an alarm sounded. The computer received a signal telling it that there was a low oil level in a gearbox. The computer did as it had been told: sounded an alarm and left the controls as they were. By coincidence, a catalyst had just been added to the reactor and the computer had just started to increase the cooling water flow to the reflux condenser. The computer kept the flow at a low value. The reactor overheated, the relief valve lifted, and the contents of the reactor were discharged to atmosphere.

The operators responded to the alarm by looking for the cause of the low oil level. They established that the level was normal and that the low-level signal was false, but by this time the reactor had overheated. A hazard and operability study had been done on the plant but those concerned did not understand what went on inside the computer and treated it as a 'black box' — something that will do what we want it to do without the need to understand

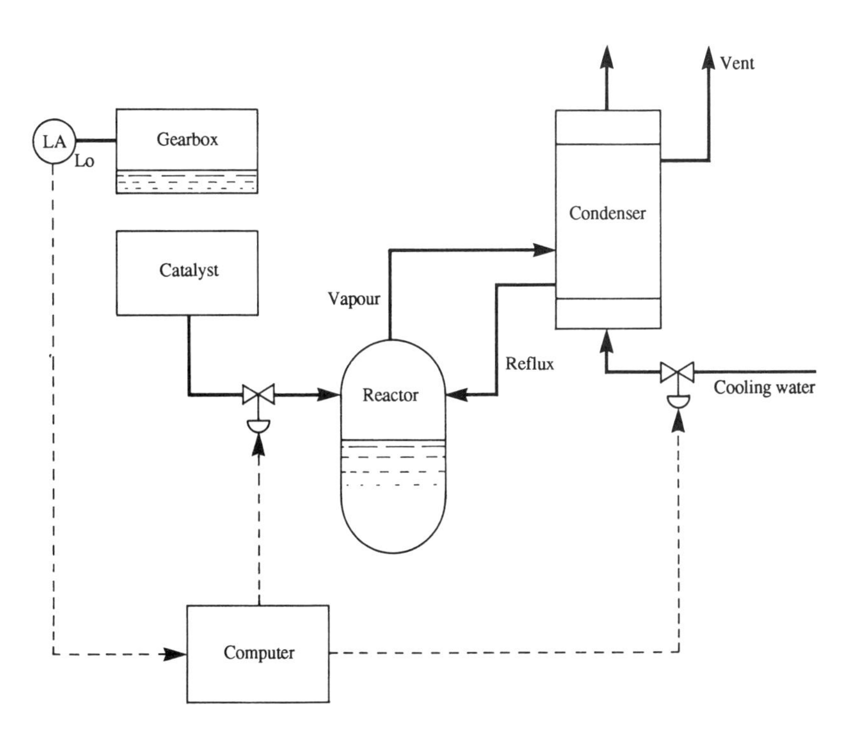

Figure 2.11 Computer-controlled batch reactor.

what goes on inside it. They did not hazop the instructions to the computer.

What they should have done is:

(1) Ask precisely what action the computer will take for all possible deviations (reverse flow, more flow, loss of power, loss of input or output signal, etc).

(2) Ask what the consequences will be.

(3) If the consequences are hazardous or prevent efficient operation, consider what alternative instructions might be given to the computer or what independent back-up system might be required.

The incident provides a good example of the results of blanket instructions (to computers or people) such as 'When a fault develops, do this'. All faults should be considered separately during a hazop, for all operating modes. The action to be taken during start-up may be different from that to be taken during normal running or later in a batch. This is a lot of work, but is unavoidable if accidents are to be prevented.

As technologists we like to know how machines work and like to take them to bits. We should extend this curiosity to computer programs and not treat them as 'black boxes'. It is not necessary to understand all the details of the electronics, but it *is* necessary to understand the details of the logic — to know precisely what instructions have been given to the computer.

There may have been a misunderstanding between the operating manager and the applications engineer. When the manager asked for all controlled variables to be left as they are when an alarm sounds, did he mean that the cooling-water flow should remain steady or that the temperature should remain steady? As stated in Section 2.2, when a computer-controlled plant is 'hazoped' the applications engineer should be a member of the team.

An amusing example of a failure to consider all eventualities occurred during the night when summertime ended. An operator put the clock on a computer back one hour. The computer then shut the plant down for an hour until the clock caught up with the program[17].

Reference 12 gives other examples of incidents on computer-controlled plants that could have been prevented by hazops.

A2.7 ABBEYSTEAD: AN EXPLOSION IN A WATER PUMPING STATION

At Abbeystead water was pumped from one river to another through a tunnel. In an incident in May 1984, when pumping stopped some water was allowed to drain out of the tunnel leaving a void. Methane from the rocks below accumulated in the void and, when pumping was restarted, was pushed through vent valves into a pumphouse where it exploded, killing 16 people, most of them local residents who were visiting the plant.

If anyone had realised that methane might be present, the explosion could have been prevented by keeping the tunnel full of water or by discharging the vent valves into the open air. In addition, smoking, the probable cause of ignition, could have been prohibited (though we should not rely on this alone). None of these things were done because no-one realised that methane might be present. Published papers contain references to the presence of dissolved methane in water supplies but these references were not known to the water supply engineers. The knowledge was in the wrong place[11].

Could a hazop have prevented the accident? Only if one of the team knew or suspected that methane might be present. He need not have known the details so long as he could recall the fact from the depths of his memory. As mentioned in Section 2.2, good hazop team members are people who have accumulated, by experience and reading, a mental ragbag of bits and pieces of knowledge that may come in useful one day. A hazop provides opportunities for the recall of long-forgotten bits of knowledge that might otherwise never pass through the conscious mind again.

A2.8 THE SELLAFIELD LEAK

A *cause célèbre* in 1983 was a leak of radioactive material into the sea from the British Nuclear Fuels Limited (BNFL) plant at Sellafield, Cumbria. It was the subject of two official reports[6,7] which agreed that the discharge was due to human error, though it is not entirely clear whether the error was due to lack of communication between shifts, poor training or wrong judgement. Both official reports failed to point out that the leak was the result of a simple design error that would have been detected by a hazard and operability study, if one had been carried out.

As a result of the human error some material which was not suitable for discharge to sea was moved to the sea tanks (see Figure 2.12 on page 46). This should not have mattered as BNFL thought they had 'second chance' design, the ability to pump material back from the sea tanks to the plant. Unfortunately the return route used part of the discharge line to sea. The return line was 2 inches diameter, the sea line was 10 inches diameter, so solids settled out in the sea line where the linear flow rate was low and were later washed out to sea. The design looks as if it might have been the result of a modification. Whether it was or not, it is the sort of design error that would be picked up by a hazard and operability study.

At a meeting where I suggested this someone doubted it, so I asked three experienced hazop team leaders if they agreed. All three said that a competent team should pick up the design error but they suggested different ways in which this would be done. I describe them here to demonstrate that a

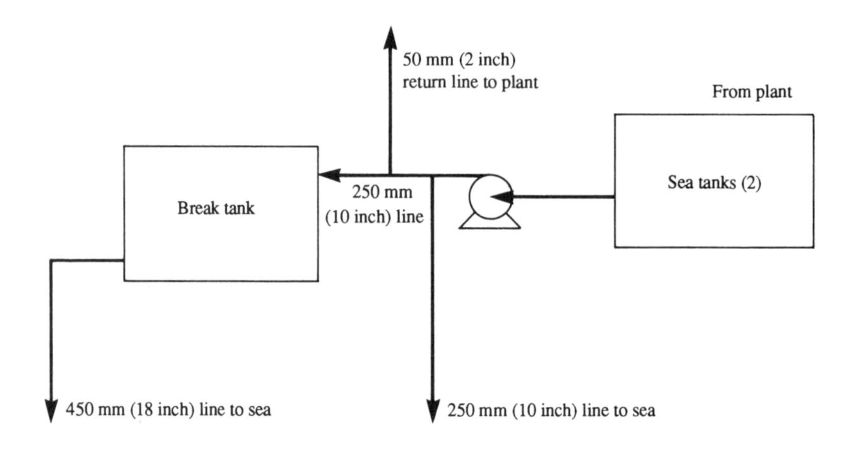

Figure 2.12 Simplified line diagram of the waste disposal system at Sellafield.

point missed while considering one deviation can often be picked up under another. (There is some redundancy in hazop.)

TEAM LEADER 1

'I feel sure that the cause described would have been identified by a hazop with a competent team.

'This is because, when studying the recycle mode of operation for reprocessing of off-spec waste product, the team's attention would be focussed on the very important matter of achieving complete transfer of the material, including the contents of the common section of line, back to the plant. If the off-spec waste product happened to be a solution, questions would be asked on, for example, the effectiveness of water displacement by flushing back to the plant. If the off-spec waste product happened to be a solid/liquid mixture (as for the case in point), questions would similarly be asked on the effectiveness of water flushing of the 10 inch line bearing in mind the restriction to flow via the 2 inch downstream system, and also possible changes in elevation. In the latter case, the team would also be particularly concerned with how to wash the off-spec solid out of the sea tank. For such a hazardous system, attention would, in fact, be focussed throughout on how best to get all the solid safely back to the plant for reprocessing.

'The final outcome of a hazop on this system would probably be to opt for an entirely independent return line from the sea tanks to the plant, thereby not only avoiding the common line section, but also reducing the chance of inadvertent discharge of off-spec waste to sea via passing or wrongly opened valves.'

TEAM LEADER 2

'One can never be absolutely certain that all possible situations are considered during a hazop, but I feel reasonably certain that this operability problem would have been discussed in some detail (providing the technique was applied by experienced people) under one or more of the following headings:

(a) NO FLOW: One reason for 'No flow' in the 2 inch line could be wrong routing — for example, all the off-spec material entering the sea due to leaking valves, incorrect valve operation, etc. How would we know that we were putting off-spec material into the sea?

(b) LESS FLOW: Again, leaking valves would allow off-spec material into the sea, and a reduced flow to the plant, etc. Also, possible restriction or blockage due to settlement of solids would certainly be discussed.

(c) MORE FLOW: The team would have checked design flow rates and commented on the different velocities in the 10 inch and 2 inch line sections and possible consequences.

(d) COMPOSITION CHANGE/CONTAMINATION: The team would have questioned methods of analysis, where samples were taken, and how we ensured that the contents of both the sea tank and the 10 inch line section were suitable to dump into the sea. Indeed, when the 10 inch route to the sea was studied the problem of contamination would again be discussed.

(e) SAFETY: Environmental considerations would have again made the team ask how we would know that the material being dumped was safe, and what were the consequences of dumping unsafe material?'

TEAM LEADER 3

'I believe that the line of questioning would be as follows:

(a) NO FLOW: Misrouting — opening of 10 inch sea line in error when material should be returned to the plant for reprocessing; this would raise further points of sampling, valve locations and the need for interlocks.

(b) REVERSE FLOW: Direct connection between plant and sea via the common manifold — what prevents backflow and how reliable is the system?

(c) LESS FLOW: Contamination — implications of incomplete purging of the system between batch discharges. How will the operators know that the sea tank and discharge line have been emptied and purged following a discharge? What

are the consequences of contamination due to accumulation of material in dead spaces in the common discharge system? A team with knowledge of slurry-handling plants would be aware of the problems of deposition resulting from reduced flow velocities. For example, it is common practice to provide recirculating ring mains on centrifuge feed systems to avoid deposition and blockage.
(d) MORE TEMPERATURE: Again, a team with knowledge of slurry handling would raise comments on solubility effects.
(e) PART OF: The team would ask how the operator would know that the end point had been established.'

I raised these questions myself. With an experienced team more points would be raised.

Settling of a solid when the linear flow rate is reduced is a well-known hazard. When the River Irwell was diverted into the Manchester Ship Canal, George E. Davis, one of the founders of chemical engineering, forecast that the canal and the lower reaches of the river would form a large settling tank and organic material would putrefy. In the summer after the canal opened the smell was so bad that passenger boat traffic was abandoned[13].

A2.9 FORMATION OF SEPARATE LAYERS

Reaction product was stored in a feed vessel until it could be batch distilled. Water used for washing out some equipment passed through two closed but leaking valves into the feed vessel. Some water was always present and was removed early in the distillation when the temperature was low. On this occasion, so much water was present that, unknown to the operators, it formed a separate, upper layer in the feed vessel (Figure 2.13). The lower layer was pumped into the distillation column first and the water in it removed. The temperature in the column then rose. When the upper layer was pumped into the column an unexpected (and previously unknown) reaction occurred between water and a solvent. The product of this reaction was recycled to the reactor with the recovered solvent where it caused a runaway reaction and an explosion. The chemistry involved is described in References 14 and 15.

This incident shows that hazop teams should pay particular attention to the following points:

• What will be the consequence of adding water (or adding more water if it is normally present)? This question should always be asked because unwanted water can so easily turn up as the result of corrosion, leaking valves, failure to disconnect a hose or accumulation in a dead-end or because it has been left behind after a wash-out.

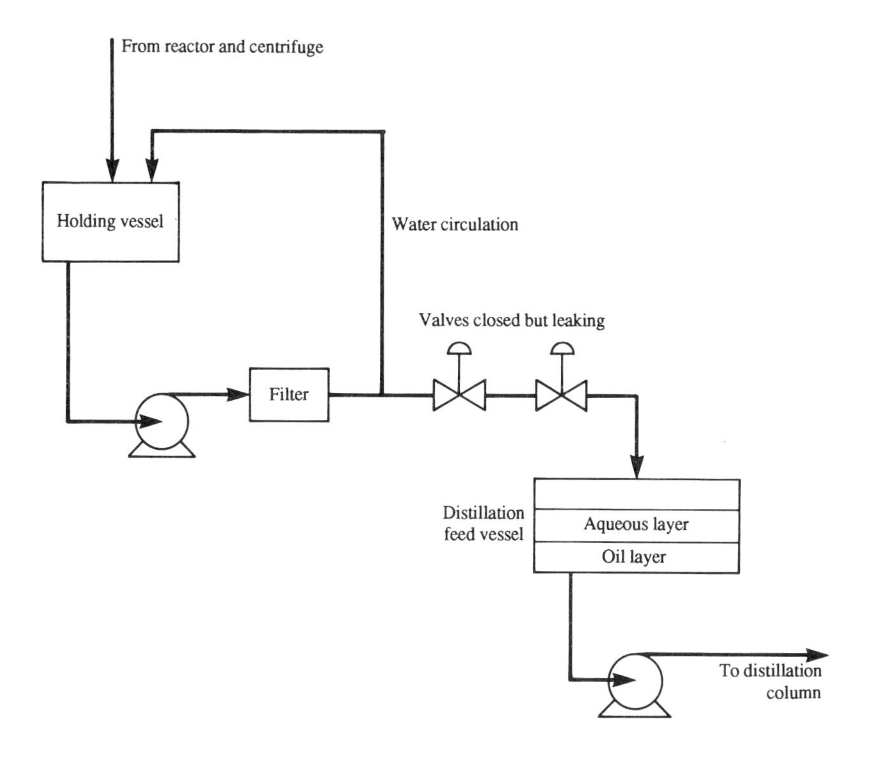

Figure 2.13 Water entered the feed vessel through leaking valves.

- Can the presence of water (or anything else) cause formation of a separate layer and, if so, what will be the consequence?
- For any deviation, look for consequences in other parts of the plant and at later times, not just for local and immediate ones (see Section 2.5(1)).

Unexpected formation of a separate layer was the cause of one of the few serious criticality incidents that have occurred on nuclear processing plants. In 1958, at Los Alamos, USA, the liquid in four tanks had to be washed with solvent to recover some plutonium. Each tank should have been treated separately but instead their contents were combined in a single tank, together with plutonium residues that had accumulated in the tanks over a period of seven years. The acid present in one of the streams caused an emulsion to break and the plutonium concentrated in the upper layer. This layer was too thin to be critical but when the stirrer was started up the layer became thicker near the axis of the stirrer and criticality occurred. One man was killed. Afterwards unnecessary transfer lines were blocked to reduce opportunities for incorrect movements[16].

A review of criticality incidents shows that many could have been prevented by hazop as they were due to reliance on valves which leaked, excessive complication, unforeseen flows through temporary lines, inadvertent siphoning and entrainment[16].

A2.10 A HAZARD NOT FORESEEN BY HAZOP

To conclude this Appendix, an account of an incident not foreseen during the hazop will illustrate a limitation of the technique (see also Section 2.7).

A plant was fitted with blowdown valves which were operated by high-pressure gas. On a cold day, a leak on the plant caught fire. The operators isolated the feed and tried to blow off the pressure in the plant. The blowdown valves failed to open as there was some water in the impulse lines and it had frozen. As a result the fire continued for longer and caused more damage than it would otherwise have done.

How the water got into the impulse lines was at first a mystery. At a hazop two years earlier, when the plant was modified, the team were asked if water could get into the impulse lines and they said 'No'.

Occasionally the valves had to be operated during a shutdown, when no high-pressure gas was available. The maintenance team were asked to operate the valves but not told how to do so. They used water and a hydraulic pump. None of the hazop team, which included the operator shop steward, knew that the valves had been operated in this way.

Hazops are only as good as the knowledge and experience of the people present. If they do not know what goes on, the hazop cannot bring out the hazards.

ACKNOWLEDGEMENTS

Thanks are due to Messrs. H.G. Lawley, F.R. Mitchell and R. Parvin for assistance with Section A2.8, and to the *Journal of Loss Prevention in the Process Industries* for permission to quote items A2.3–5 which originally appeared in Vol 4 (2), January 1991, p. 128.

REFERENCES IN APPENDIX TO CHAPTER 2

1. Troyan, J.E. and Le Vine, L.Y., 1968, *Loss Prevention*, 2: 125.
2. Oliveria, D.B., March 1973, *Hydrocarbon Processing*, 52 (3): 112.
3. Kletz, T.A., 1988, *What went wrong? Case histories of chemical plant disasters*, 2nd edition, Gulf Publishing Co., Houston, Texas, Chapter 18.

4. Union Carbide Corporation, Danbury, Connecticut, USA, March 1985, *Bhopal methyl isocyanate incident investigation team report*.
5. Kletz, T.A., 1991, *Plant design for safety —a user-friendly approach*, Hemisphere, New York.
6. Health and Safety Executive, 1984, *The contamination of the beach incident at BNFL Sellafield.*
7. Department of the Environment, London, 1984, *An incident leading to contamination of the beaches near to the BNFL Windscale and Calder Works*.
8. Kalelkar, A.S., 1988, Investigations of large magnitude incidents, *Symposium Series No. 110*, Institution of Chemical Engineers, Rugby, UK, 553.
9. Hill, R., January 1988, *Journal of Loss Prevention in the Process Industries*, 1 (1): 25.
10. Gibson, T.O., October 1989, *Plant/Operations Progress*, 8 (4): 209.
11. Health and Safety Executive, 1985, *The Abbeystead explosion*, HMSO, London.
12. Kletz, T.A., January 1991, *Plant/Operations Progress*, 10 (1): 17.
13. Stainthorp, F., 23 August 1990, *The Chemical Engineer*, No. 480, 16.
14. Mooney, D.G., 1991, An overview of the Shell fluoroaromatics plant explosion, *Symposium Series No. 124*, Institution of Chemical Engineers, Rugby, UK, 381.
15. Kletz, T.A., August 1991, *Loss Prevention Bulletin*, No. 100, 21.
16. Stratton, W.E., 1989, *A review of criticality accidents*, US Dept of Energy, Report No. DOE/NCT-04.
17. Wray, A.M., 8 September 1988, *New Scientist*.

3. HAZARD ANALYSIS (HAZAN)

'When you can measure what you are speaking about and express it in numbers, you know something about it.'
Lord Kelvin

3.1 OBJECTIVE

The objective of this Chapter is to help readers carry out their own hazard analyses — that is, to apply quantitative methods to safety problems. You cannot, however, expect a brief guide like this to make you fully competent. You should discuss your first attempts with an experienced analyst.

Hazard analysis is not an esoteric technique that can be practised only by those who have served an apprenticeship in the art. It can be practised by any competent technologist provided he discusses his first attempts with someone more experienced (see Section 4.10).

Assessing a hazard, by hazard analysis or any other technique, should be our second choice. Whenever we can we should avoid the hazard by changing the design[27] (see Section 2.7). Many books and courses on hazard analysis fail to make this clear. They seem to assume that the hazard is unavoidable and therefore we should estimate the probability that it will occur and its consequences and make them as low as is required by our criteria (or, to use the legal phrase, as low as reasonably practicable) (see Section 3.3). They rarely point out that it is often possible to avoid a hazard. Of course, we cannot always do so; it is often impossible or too expensive.

3.2 WHY DO WE WANT TO APPLY NUMERICAL METHODS TO SAFETY PROBLEMS?

The horizontal axis of Figure 3.1 shows expenditure on safety over and above that necessary for a workable plant, and the vertical axis shows the money we get back in return. In the left-hand area safety is good business — by spending money on safety, apart from preventing injuries, our plants blow up or burn down less often and we make more profit.

In the next area safety is poor business — we get some money back for our safety expenditure but not as much as we would get by investing our money in other ways.

If we go on spending money on safety we move into the third area where safety is bad business but good humanity — money is spent so that people do not get hurt and we do not expect to get any material profit back in return — and finally into the fourth area where we are spending so much on safety that we go out of business. Our products become so expensive that no-one will buy them;

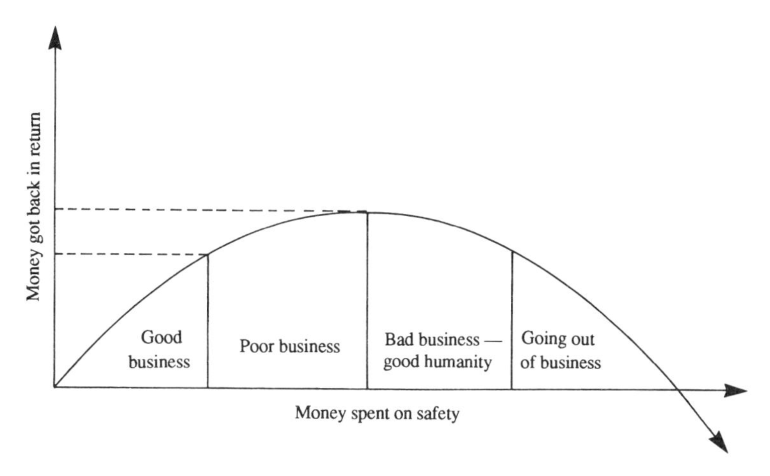

Figure 3.1 The effects of increasing expenditure on safety.

our company is bankrupt and we are out of a job. The public are deprived of the benefits they could get from our products. We have to decide where to draw the line between the last two areas. Usually this is a qualitative judgement but it is often possible to make it quantitative. The methods for doing so are known as hazard analysis or hazan.

They are called *hazard* analysis rather than risk analysis as risk analysis is used to describe methods of estimating commercial risks (see References 1 and 2 and Section 1.2) and hazard *analysis* because, as we shall see, an essential step is breaking down the events leading to the hazard into their constituent steps.

While hazop is a technique that can, and I think should, be applied to every new design and major modification, hazan is, as stated in Section 1.1, a selective technique. It is neither necessary nor possible to quantify every hazard on every plant. Unfortunately the apparent precision of hazan appeals to the legislative mind and in some countries the authorities have suggested that every hazard should be quantified.

Hazan is not, of course, a technique for showing that expenditure on additional safety measures is necessary. Often it shows that the hazard is small and that further expenditure is unnecessary.

Hazan does more than tell us the size of a risk. Especially when fault trees (Section 3.5.9) are used, it shows how the hazard arises, which contributing factors are the most important and which are the most effective ways of reducing the risk. Most of all, it helps us to allocate our resources in the most effective way. If we deal with each problem as it arises, the end result may be the opposite of that intended. This is common in politics[28] and can also occur in engineering. It can result in massive expenditure on preventing a repetition of the last accident while greater risks, which have not so far caused injury, are unrecognised and ignored.

3.3 THE STAGES OF HAZARD ANALYSIS

Every hazard analysis, however simple, consists of three steps:

(i) Estimating how often the incident will occur.

(ii) Estimating the consequences to:

- employees;
- the public and the environment;
- plant and profits.

In both (i) and (ii), whenever possible, estimates should be based on past experience. However, sometimes there is no past experience, either because the design is new or the incident has never happened, and in these cases we have to use synthetic methods. By combining the probability of an incident and the size of the consequences we are able to compare infrequent but serious incidents with more frequent but less serious incidents.

(iii) Comparing the results of (i) and (ii) with a target or criterion in order to decide whether or not action to reduce the probability of occurrence or minimise the consequences is desirable, or whether the hazard can be ignored, at least for the time being.

The methods used in step (i) are probabilistic. We estimate how often, on average, the incident will occur but not when it will occur.

The methods used in step (ii) are partly probabilistic, partly deterministic. For example, if there is a leak of flammable gas, we can only estimate the probability that it will ignite. If it does we can estimate the heat radiation and the way in which it will attenuate with distance (deterministic). If a person is exposed to the radiation, we can estimate the probability that death or certain degrees of injury will occur. At high levels deaths are certain and the estimate is deterministic. High levels of radioactivity cause burns (deterministic). At low levels the probability of disease, not the seriousness of the disease, increases with the dose.

In the following pages we first discuss step (iii), then step (i). Discussion of step (ii) is not attempted. The methods used differ for each type of hazard — fires, explosions and releases of toxic gas — and the number of calculation methods available is enormous; for example, over a hundred methods for calculating gas dispersion have been published[49]. Reference should be made to specialist textbooks or to *Lees*. Computer programs are now available for carrying out these consequence analyses and in the more sophisticated programs the results are combined with estimates of probability and risk contours are drawn. For an example, see Reference 25.

The biggest uncertainty in step (ii) is determining the size of the leak. Gas dispersion or explosion overpressure calculations are often carried out with great accuracy although the amount of material leaking out can only be guessed. Withers is one of the few authors who has provided estimates of the probability of leaks of various magnitude[29].

Many writers are reluctant to discuss step (iii) but it is little use knowing that a plant will blow up once in 1000 years with a 50% chance that someone will be killed, unless we can use this information to help us decide whether we should reduce the probability (or protect people from the consequences) or whether the risk is so small, compared with all the other risks around us, that we should ignore it and devote our attention to bigger risks.

Who should answer the three questions? The first two questions can only be answered by expert knowledge, or by expert judgement if information is lacking. The third question is a matter on which everybody, and especially those exposed to the risk, has a right to comment. The expert has a duty to provide information on comparative risks, in a way that his audience can understand, but has no greater right than anyone else to decide what risks other people should accept. If the public wish to spend money on removing what the expert thinks is a trivial risk, they have a right, in a democracy, to do so. In the end it is the public's money that is spent, not a company's or the government's, as the cost is passed on to them through prices or taxes (see Section 3.4.4).

In the United States companies are less willing than in the UK to propose targets for tolerable risk. In the UK there is a long-standing tradition that a company is not expected to do everything possible to reduce a risk, only what is 'reasonably practicable'; hazard analysis is an attempt to quantify this phrase. In the US there is much more pressure to remove every risk, and companies are reluctant to admit that they cannot do so and that there is a low level of risk that they regard as acceptable or tolerable (see Section 3.4).

In practice, of course, the decision whether or not to reduce a particular hazard will usually be made by the responsible manager, taking into account any generally accepted or company criteria, the views of employees and the public and, of course, the views of the factory inspectorate or other regulatory authority. However, the hazard analyst who calculates the probability and consequences of the hazard should not merely display them to the manager but should say what he thinks should be done. The manager does not have to accept the analyst's views but the analyst, like all experts, should not merely provide information and display alternatives but should make clear recommendations. Only when he does so can he expect a salary comparable with that of the manager he advises.

In brief, the stages in hazard analysis are:

(i) How often?
(ii) How big?
(iii) So what?

If you can remember these six words you will know what to do (though not how to do it) if you are ever asked to carry out a hazard analysis. You will also know what to look for in hazard analyses carried out by others (see Chapter 4).

3.4 SOME OF THE TARGETS OR CRITERIA

When injury is unlikely we can compare the annual cost of preventing an accident with the average annual cost of the accident. Suppose an accident will cause £1M worth of damage and is estimated to occur once in 1000 years, an average cost of £1000/year. Then it is worth spending up to £1000/year to prevent it but not more. Capital costs can be converted to maintenance, depreciation and interest. Future costs should be discounted, although the data are often not accurate enough to make this worthwhile (but see Section 6.1, last paragraph).

This method could be used for all accidents if we could put a value on injuries and life, but there is no generally agreed figure for them (see Section 3.4.7). So instead we set a target.

For example, in fixing the height of handrails round a place of work, the law does not ask us to compare the cost of fitting them with the value of the lives of the people who would otherwise fall off. It fixes a height for the handrails (36 inches to 45 inches). A sort of intuitive hazan shows that with handrails of this height the chance of falling over them, though not zero, is so small that we are justified in ignoring it. Similarly, we fix a 'height' or level for the risk to life.

In setting this level we should remember that we are all at risk all the time, whatever we do, even staying at home. We accept the risks when we consider that, by doing so, something worthwhile is achieved. We go rock climbing or sailing or we smoke because we consider the pleasure is worth the risk. We take jobs as airline pilots or soldiers or we become missionaries among cannibals because we consider that the pay, or the interest of the job, or the benefit it brings to others, makes the risk worthwhile.

At work there is likely to be a slight risk, whatever we do to remove known risks. By accepting this risk we earn our living and we make goods that enable us and others to lead a fuller life.

A widely-used target for the risk to life of employees discussed in the next section, is the Fatal Accident Rate (FAR). Risks to the public are discussed in Section 3.4.4.

But it is not always necessary to estimate the risk to life. When we are making a change it is often sufficient to say that the new design must be as safe as, preferably safer than, that which has been generally accepted without complaint. For example:

- If trips are used instead of relief valves they should have a probability of failure 10 times lower[3,4].
- If equipment which might cause ignition is introduced into a Zone 2 area it should be no more likely to spark than the electrical equipment already there.
- A new form of transport should be no more hazardous, preferably less hazardous, than the old form.

For other examples, see Section 3.4.8.

Risks which are within a target or criterion are sometimes called 'acceptable risks' but I do not like this phrase. We have no right to decide what risks are acceptable to other people and we should never knowingly fail to act when other people's lives are at risk; but we cannot do everything at once — we have to set priorities.

More pragmatically, particularly when talking to a wider audience than fellow technologists, the use of the phrase 'acceptable risk' often causes people to take exception. 'What right have you,' they say, 'to decide what risks are acceptable to me?' But everyone has problems with priorities; most people realise that we cannot do everything at once, and they are more likely to listen if we talk about priorities.

The UK Health and Safety Executive proposes[30] that the phrase 'tolerable risk' should be used instead of 'acceptable risk'. 'Tolerable' has been defined[31] as 'that which is borne, albeit reluctantly, while "acceptable" denotes some higher degree of approbation'.

The UK Health and Safety Executive also proposes that instead of one level of risk there should be two: an upper level which is never exceeded and a lower or negligible level which there is no need to get below. In between the risk should be reduced if it is reasonably practicable to do so. Risks near the upper level should be tolerated only when reduction is impracticable or grossly disproportionate to the cost (see Figure 3.2 on page 58; note that in this figure 'Negligible risk' should be lower down the page than the 'Broadly acceptable region'). Cost-benefit analysis, comparing the cost of reducing a hazard with the benefits, should be used to determine whether or not an action is reasonably practicable[30,32]. The HSE report seems to imply that, for risks to the public, the ratio between the upper and lower criteria should be about a hundred (see Section 3.4.6).

We do not, of course, remove priority problems by asking for more resources. We merely move the target level to a different point.

Apart from the main uses of hazard analysis in helping us decide whether or not expenditure on particular safety measures is justified — that is, in helping us set priorities — it can also help us to:

- resolve design choices, for example, between relief valves and instrumented protective systems (trips);

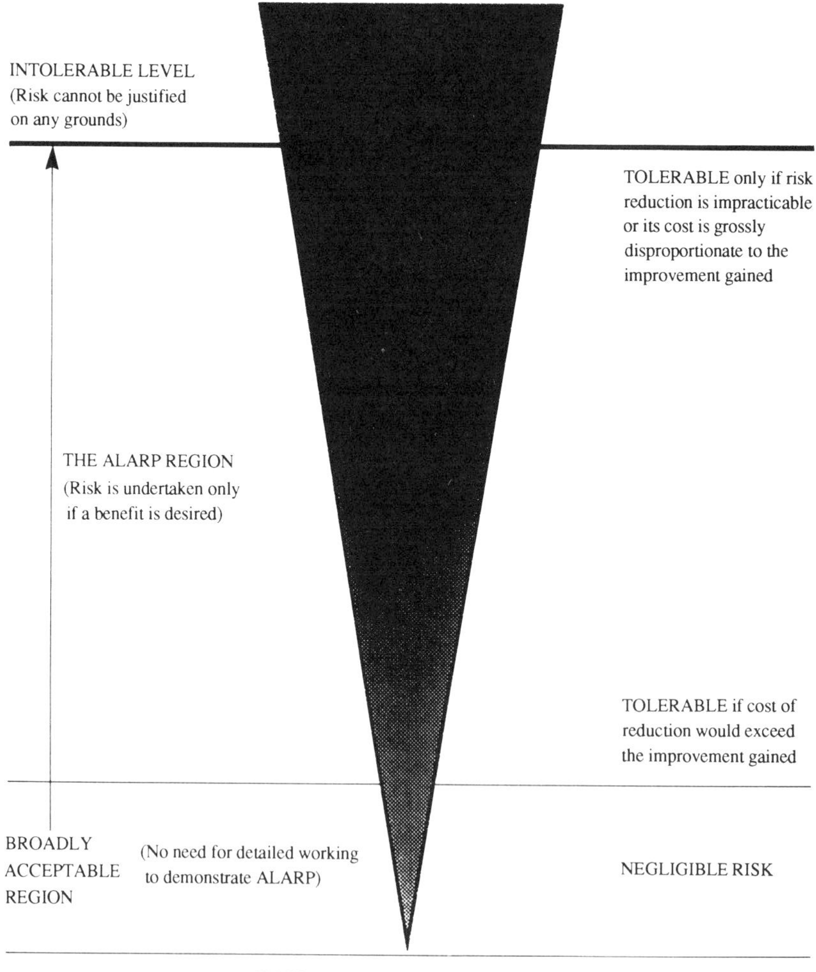

Figure 3.2 Levels of risk and ALARP. (Reproduced by permission of the Health & Safety Commission.)

- decide how much redundancy or diversity (see Section 3.6.4) to build into a protective system;
- set testing, inspection and maintenance schedules (see Section 3.5.3).

As mentioned in Section 1.2, the Institution of Chemical Engineers defines[33] hazard analysis as 'the identification of undesired events that lead to the materialisation of a hazard, the analysis of the mechanisms by which these undesired events could occur and usually the estimation of the extent, magnitude and likelihood of any harmful effects'.

According to this definition hazard analysis includes the identification of hazards (considered in Chapter 2) and stages (i) and (ii) above, but not stage (iii). The report suggests that what I call hazard analysis should be called risk assessment. As already stated, stages (i) and (ii) are pointless unless we also carry out stage (iii).

If you are asked to carry out a hazard analysis or you ask someone else to carry one out, make sure that you both understand what is meant by these words.

3.4.1 RISKS TO EMPLOYEES — THE FATAL ACCIDENT RATE (FAR)

FAR is defined as the number of fatal accidents in a group of 1000 men in a working lifetime (10^8 hours). Table 3.1 on page 60 shows some typical figures.

For weekly-paid employees in the chemical industry the FAR is about 4 (the same as the average for all activities covered by the UK Factories Act).* This is made up of:

- ordinary industrial risks (eg falling downstairs or getting run over): 2;
- chemical risks (eg fire, toxic release or spillage of corrosive chemical): 2.

If we are sure that we have identified all the chemical risks attached to a particular job, we say that the man doing the job should not be exposed, for these chemical risks, to a FAR greater than 2. We will eliminate or reduce, as a matter of priority, any such risks on new or existing plants.

It would be wrong to spend our resources on reducing the risk to people who are already exposed to below average risks. Instead we should give priority to those risks which are above average.

---

* If you spend your working lifetime in a typical factory of 1000 men, then during your time there 4 of your fellow workers will be killed in industrial accidents, but about 20 will be killed in other accidents (mostly on the roads and in the home) and about 370 will die from disease, including about 40 from the results of smoking, if present rates continue.

Often we are not sure that we have identified all the chemical risks and so we say that any single one, considered in isolation, should not expose an employee to a FAR greater than 0.4. We will eliminate or reduce, as a matter of priority, any hazard on a new or existing plant that exceeds this figure. We are thus assuming that there are about five significant chemical risks on a typical plant.

Experience has shown that the costs of doing this, though often substantial, are not unbearable. They may involve the company in an expenditure

TABLE 3.1
FARs for some UK industries 1974–78

	FAR	Risk per person per year
Offshore oil and gas	82	165×10^{-5}
Deep sea fishing	44	88×10^{-5}
Coal mining	10	20×10^{-5}
Construction	7.5	17.5×10^{-5}
Shipbuilding and marine engineering	5.25	10.5×10^{-5}
Chemical and allied industries	4.25	8.5×10^{-5}
All premises covered by the Factories Act	≅4	$\cong 8 \times 10^{-5}$
All manufacturing industry	1.15	2.3×10^{-5}
Vehicle manufacture	0.75	1.5×10^{-5}
Clothing manufacture	0.25	0.5×10^{-5}

Notes:

- The FAR is the number of fatal accidents in 10^8 hours or a group of 1000 men in a working lifetime.
- All figures have been taken from Reference 34 except for those for deep sea fishing, all manufacturing industry and all premises covered by the Factories Act (which includes construction). The first two of these have been taken from Reference 30 and refer to the 1980s.
- The figure for the chemical industry includes the 28 people killed at Flixborough and is higher than for other 5 year periods.
- The FAR for construction erectors is about ten times higher than the figure quoted for the construction industry as a whole.

which some of its competitors do not incur. Some of the extra expenditure can be recouped in lower insurance premiums; some can be recouped by the greater plant reliability which safety measures often produce; the rest is a self-imposed 'tax' which has to be balanced by greater efficiency.

Note that when estimating a FAR for comparison with the target we should estimate the FAR for the person or group at highest risk, not the average for all the employees on the plant. It would be no consolation to me, if I complained that I was exposed to a high risk, to be told, 'Don't worry. The average for you and your fellow workers is low'. It may be all right for them but it certainly is not for me.

As mentioned in Section 3.4, the HSE has proposed upper and lower limits. Their upper limit for employees is a risk of death of 10^{-3} per year (FAR 50) which seems rather high. However, they justify it on the grounds that some risks at about this level are tolerated in practice.

3.4.2 CONVERTING FAR TO HAZARD RATE

The hazard (or incident) rate is the rate at which dangerous incidents occur. Suppose the man at greatest risk is killed every time the dangerous incident occurs (this is an example, not a typical situation), then it must not occur more often than:

0.4 incident in 10^8 working hours or

once in 2.5×10^8 working hours

= 30 000 years

or 3×10^{-5} incident/year, ie the probability of occurrence should not exceed 3×10^{-5}/year (for a shift job).

For a job manned only during day hours the corresponding figures are once in 120 000 years or 8×10^{-6} incident/year.

If the man at greatest risk is killed every 10th time the incident occurs then the target hazard rate is:

once in 3000 years or

3×10^{-4} occasion/year

and so on.

3.4.3 MULTIPLE CASUALTIES

What is the target hazard rate if more than one person is killed?

Consider two cases:

(A) One person is killed every year for 100 years.

(B) 100 people are killed once in 100 years.

Should the prevention of (B) have higher priority than the prevention of (A), or vice versa?

The arguments in favour of giving priority to the prevention of (B) are:

- The press, public and Parliament make more fuss about (B), whilst they usually ignore (A). The public 'perceive' (B) as worse; as servants of the public we must therefore give priority to the prevention of (B).
- (B) disrupts the organisation and the local community and the wounds take longer to heal. It may cause production to be halted for a long time, perhaps for ever, and new requirements may be introduced.

Various writers have therefore proposed that the tolerable hazard rate for (B) should be the tolerable hazard rate for (A) divided by $\log N$, or N or N^2, where N is the number of people killed per incident. However, these formulae are quite arbitrary and if we divide the hazard rate by N^2, or even N, we may get such low hazard rates that they are impossible to achieve.

Gibson[5] has suggested that we can allow for the wider effects by estimating the financial costs of disruption of production, etc, and comparing them with the costs of prevention. This may be a more effective and defensible method than introducing arbitrary factors.

It is true that as servants of the public we should do what they want, but a good servant does not obey unthinkingly; he points out the consequences of his instructions. If we think the public's perception of risks is wrong, we should say so, and say why we think so. Perhaps the public think that preventing events like (B) will reduce the number of people killed accidentally; it would actually have very little effect on the total number killed.

The argument in favour of giving priority to the prevention of (A) is that (B) will probably never happen (if the plant lasts 10 years the odds are 10 to 1 against) but that (A) almost certainly will happen — one person will probably be killed every year — so why not give priority to preventing the deaths of those who will probably be killed, rather than to preventing events which will probably never happen? This argument becomes stronger if we consider case (C):

(C) 1000 people are killed once in 1000 years. In this case it is 100 to 1 that nobody will be killed during the life of the plant.

The simplest and fairest view seems to be to give equal priority to the prevention of (A) and (B) — we're just as dead in case (A) as in case (B).

If we give priority to the prevention of (B) we are taking resources away from the prevention of (A) and, in effect, saying to the people who will be killed one at a time that we consider their deaths as less important than others. We should treat all men the same.

There may, however, be an economic argument for preventing (B), as argued by Gibson, even though the risk is so small that we would not normally spend resources on reducing it further.

Consider now two more cases:

(D) A plant blows up once in 1000 years killing the single operator.

(E) A similar plant, less automated, also blows up once in 1000 years but kills all 10 operators. The FAR is the same in both cases, the risk to all 11 operators is the same but some way of drawing attention to the higher exposure involved in Case (E) is desirable. Lees[6] suggests that the number killed, the accident fatality number, should be quoted as well as the FAR.

3.4.4 RISKS TO THE PUBLIC

Table 3.2 on page 64 shows the risk of death, per year, for a number of non-occupational activities, including activities such as driving and smoking that we accept voluntarily and others that are imposed on us without our permission. The figures are approximate and should be used with caution. Nevertheless they show that we accept voluntarily activities that expose us to risks of 10^{-5} or more per year, sometimes a lot more, while many of the involuntary risks are much lower. We accept, with little or no complaint, a number of involuntary risks (for example, from lightning or falling aircraft) which expose us to a risk of death of about 10^{-7} or less per year.

We thus have a possible basis for considering risks to the public at large from an industrial activity. If the average risk to those exposed is more than 10^{-7} per person per year, we will eliminate or reduce the risk as a matter or priority. If it is already less it would not be right to spend scarce resources on reducing the risk further. It would be like spending additional money, above that already spent, on protecting people from lightning. There are more important hazards to be dealt with first.

As well as considering the average risk we should consider the person at greatest risk. A man aged 20 years has a probability of death from all causes of 1 in 1000 per year. (The figure for a younger man is not much less.) An increase of 1% from industrial risks is hardly likely to cause him much concern, and an increase of 0.1% should certainly not do so. This gives a range of 10^{-5} to 10^{-6} per year.

Why do I suggest a lower figure (10^{-7} per year) for the average risk than the 10^{-5} to 10^{-6} range for the person at greatest risk? Consider a town of 500 000 people in which a chemical plant imposes some risk on all the inhabitants, though some of them, of course, are at greater risk than others. If the average risk is 10^{-7} per year, on average one person will be killed every twenty years; by the time a second death occurs the first one will probably have been forgotten. If the average risk is 10^{-6}, on average someone will be killed every two years and the public would consider this quite intolerable. In a

TABLE 3.2
Some non-occupational risks

	Risk of death per person per year	
Cancer	280×10^{-5}	(1 in 360)
Road accidents (UK)	10×10^{-5}	(1 in 10 000)
Road accidents (US)	24×10^{-5}	(1 in 4000)
All accidents (UK)	30×10^{-5}	(1 in 3300)
Murder (UK)	1×10^{-5}	(1 in 100 000)
Smoking 20 cigarettes/day	500×10^{-5}	(1 in 200)
Drinking (1 bottle wine/day)	75×10^{-5}	(1 in 1300)
Rock climbing (100 h/y)	400×10^{-5}	(1 in 250)
All risks, man aged 20	100×10^{-5}	(1 in 1000)
All risks, man aged 60	1000×10^{-5}	(1 in 100)
Lightning (UK)	10^{-7}	(1 in 10 million)
Release from nuclear power station (at 1 km)	10^{-7}	(1 in 10 million)
Flooding of dykes (Holland)	10^{-7}	(1 in 10 million)
Fall of aircraft (UK)	0.2×10^{-7}	(1 in 50 million)
Hit by meteorite	10^{-11}	(1 in 100 billion)

Notes:
- Most figures are taken from References 32, 34 and 35.
- Most of the risks are averaged over the whole population but are not always equally distributed; the very old and very young, for example, are more likely than others to be killed in an accident; smokers are more likely than non-smokers to get cancer.
- The figures for smoking, drinking and rock climbing apply only to those who carry out these activities.

democracy all criteria for risk (and everything else that affects them) must be acceptable to the public (see Section 5.3).

We have considered average risks and the person at greatest risk. Another way of expressing risk to the public is to draw a graph of the number of people killed *(N)* against the frequency of the event *(F)*. Figure 3.3 (from Reference 30) shows an *F–N* line for a particular chlorine installation and, for comparison, a proposed criterion (the line AB). Both lines refer to casualties, not deaths; Reference 30 suggests that about one third of them will result in death. Note that the probability that ten or a hundred people will become casualties is higher than allowed by the criterion, but that there is a limit to the possible number of casualties.

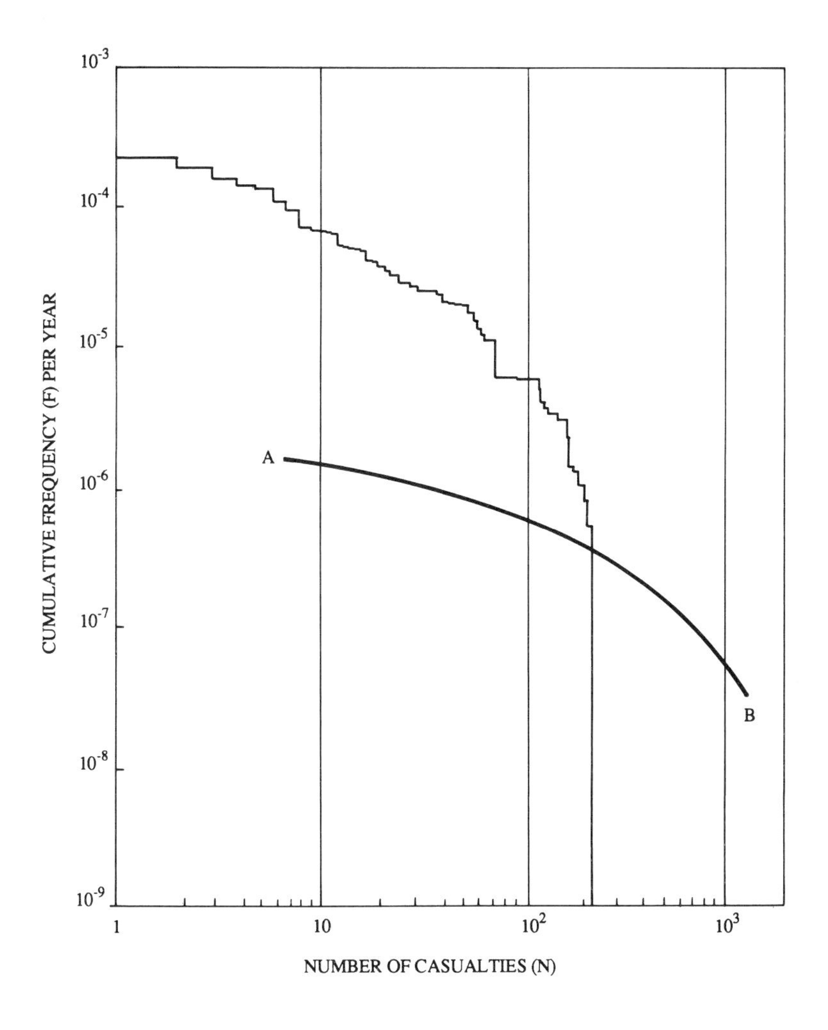

Figure 3.3 *F–N* curve for chlorine installation. AB shows a suggested criterion. (Reproduced by permission of Her Majesty's Stationery Office.)

The jagged line in Figure 3.3 is a prediction by experts of what will occur (if the assumptions on which it is based are correct); only experts in the technology are able to derive it. (In other cases the *F–N* line may be based on the historical record.) In contrast, the line AB is based on judgement; it shows the level of risk that people will, it is believed, tolerate. Everyone has a right to comment on its position, especially those exposed to the risk, and the expert has no greater right to do so than anyone else (see Section 3.3).

It is difficult to explain *F–N* curves to the public. They pick on the fact that a large number of casualties or deaths can occur but do not grasp that the probability of this happening is astronomically low. In Figure 3.3, for example, the frequency of an incident causing 100 casualties is less than 10^{-5} per year. If 100 000 people live near the chlorine installation, the chance that a particular person, picked at random, will become a casualty in such an incident is less than 10^{-8} per year. Imagine this page being so long that it stretches from London to Newcastle (about 500 km); 10^{-8} is the probability that if two people are asked to choose a line of type at random they will pick the same one. This probability is nevertheless considered too high and if the risk can can be reduced to the level shown by the target line AB, the page would have to stretch from London to New York.

Other criteria for risks to the public are reviewed in Reference 17. The criteria vary but it is generally agreed that the public should be exposed to much lower risks than employees. People choose to work for a particular company or industry but members of the public have risks imposed on them against their will. But the public are further away from the source of the hazard so in practice the risk to employees may be more important. For example, the pressure developed by an explosion decreases with distance; the risk to the public is usually so much less than the risk to employees that reducing the latter is the more important task. However, this may not be the case if houses have been built close to the factory fence.

3.4.5 WHY CONSIDER ONLY FATAL ACCIDENTS?

As pointed out by Heinrich many years ago, there is a relationship between fatal, lost-time, minor and no-injury accidents (in which only material damage is caused). If we halve fatal accidents from a particular cause, we halve lost-time accidents, minor accidents, and no-injury accidents from that cause. If we halve the number of deaths from explosions, for example, on a particular plant we probably also halve the number of lost-time accidents and minor accidents caused by explosions and the material damage they cause.

Note that halving the total number of fatal accidents in a factory will not necessarily halve the total number of lost-time (or minor) accidents, as the ratio of lost time to fatal accidents differs for different sorts of accidents. For example, it is about 250 for transport accidents, but about 20 000 for accidents involving the use of tools.

3.4.6 REMOVE FIRST THE RISKS THAT ARE CHEAPEST TO REMOVE

An alternative approach to target setting is to give priority to the expenditure which saves the most lives per £M spent[16]. This method would save more lives for a given expenditure so why do we not use it? There are three reasons:

- The first is moral. An employee or a member of the public may accept that a risk is so small, compared with other risks around us, that it is hardly worth worrying about, but he (or she) will hardly accept a risk because it is expensive to remove. It may be better for society as a whole, but not for him (or her).

Restating the same objection in other words, although we might reduce the total number of people killed in an organisation or society by concentrating the risks on a few individuals, we are not prepared to do so: we prefer to spread the risks more or less equally, or at least ensure that no-one is exposed to a level of risk that would be regarded as intolerable. Note that in industry the lives saved are notional. If we do spend money on reducing a particular risk, all we are doing is making the already low risk of an accident even lower. It is unlikely that anyone's life will actually be saved and this makes it easier to adopt the moral attitude just described. In road safety, on the other hand, we are dealing with real lives; more lives will actually be saved if we spend our money in a more cost-effective way, and in this field of activity attempts are made to spend money in ways that do save the most lives per £M spent. We do not try to equalise the risks between different categories of road user, though it could perhaps be argued that pedestrians — who are exposed against their will — should be subjected to a lower risk.

- The second reason is pragmatic. If we agree to remove risks that are cheap to remove but to accept those that are expensive to remove, then there is a temptation for every design engineer and manager to say that the risks on his plant are expensive to remove. If, however, all risks must be reduced below a certain level, then experience shows that design engineers and plant managers do find 'reasonably practicable' ways of reducing them below that level.
- A third reason is that the usual procedure in industry has always been to work to a risk criterion, not a cost one. (See the note on handrails in Section 3.4.)

Despite these comments, the cost of saving a life is useful in industry as a secondary criterion. If the notional cost of saving a life is greatly in excess of the normal for the industry, then we should not exceed the usual risk criterion, but we should look for a cheaper solution. Experience shows that in practice it can usually be found. There is usually more than one solution to every problem.

Section 3.4 suggested the use of two criteria, an upper one that should never be exceeded and a lower one of negligible risk which we need not strive to get below. In between the risk should be reduced if it is reasonably practicable to do so, and cost-benefit analysis should be used to help us decide if a particular proposal is reasonably practicable. To carry out such calculations we need to know the value to put on a life.

3.4.7 THE COST OF SAVING A LIFE

Various ways have been suggested for estimating the cost of saving a life. One is the value of a person's future contribution to society; another is the cost of damages awarded by the Courts. But the value of any article or service is not what it costs to produce it, or the future benefits it will bring, but what people are prepared to pay for it — the test of the market place. Table 3.3 summarises some of the prices that are actually paid to save a life and it will be seen that the range is enormous. Doctors can save lives for a few thousands or tens of thousands of pounds per life saved and road engineers for a few hundred thousands per life saved, while industry spends millions and the nuclear industry tens of millions (even more according to some estimates) per life saved.

Most of the values in Table 3.3 are implicit — that is, unknown to the people who authorise the expenditure, as they rarely divide the costs of their proposals by the number of lives that will be saved. No other commodity or service shows such a variation, a range of 10^6, in the price paid. (Electricity from watch batteries costs 10^5 times electricity from the mains but we pay for the convenience.)

What value then should we use in cost-benefit calculations? I suggest the typical value for the particular industry or activity (such as the chemical industry or road safety) in which we are engaged. Society as a whole might benefit if the chemical or nuclear industries spent less on safety and the money saved was given to the road engineers or to doctors, but there is no social mechanism for making the transfer. All we can do, as technologists, is to spend the resources we control to the best advantage. As citizens, of course, we can advocate a transfer of resources if we wish to do so.

The figures in Table 3.3 are very approximate. They are taken from various estimates published between 1967 and 1985, corrected to 1985 prices (for details see Reference 36), and some may have been made out of date by changes in technology. They vary over such a wide range, however, that errors introduced in this way are probably unimportant (see also Section 3.8.1).

TABLE 3.3
Some estimates of the money (£) spent to save a life

Health	Increasing tax on cigarettes	Negative
	Anti-smoking propaganda	Small
	Cervical cancer screening	6K
	Artificial kidneys	40K
	Intensive care	20K
	Liver transplants	100K
Road travel	Various schemes	20K–8M
	Schemes implemented	Up to 1M
Industry	Agriculture (employees)	10K
	Rollover protection for tractors	400K
	Steel handling (employees)	1M
	Pharmaceuticals (employees)	20M
	Pharmaceuticals (public)	50K
	Chemical industry (employees) (typical figure)	4M
	Nuclear industry (employees and public)	15–30M
Social policy	Smoke alarms	500K
	Preventing collapse of high-rise flats	100M
	Giving members of social class 5 a social class 2 income (family of 4 young people)	1M
	Third World starvation relief	10K
	Immunisation (Indonesia)	100£

Notes:

- All figures are taken from Reference 36, are corrected to 1985 prices and refer to the UK. They are approximate and some may have been outdated by changes in technology. US figures are often higher.
- A 10% increase in the tax on tobacco decreases smoking by about 5% so there is a net increase in revenue.
- If we spend £10M on anti-smoking propaganda and as a result 1000 people (less than 1 smoker in 10 000) give up smoking the cost of saving a life will be about £10K.
- The death rate (for almost all ages and causes) of members of social class 5 (unskilled occupations) is about 1.8 times that of members of social classes 1 (professional occupations) and 2 (managerial occupations). It can be argued that, in the long run, a rise in income to the social class 2 level will produce a social class 2 lifestyle.

3.4.8 COMPARING OLD AND NEW

In Section 3.4 I pointed out that instead of comparing a risk with a target or criterion we can compare alternatives. For example, a chemical intermediate was carried 200 miles by road from one plant to another for further processing. The intermediate was in the form of an aqueous solution and so was harmless, but money was being spent to transport water. It was therefore proposed to transport an alternative intermediate which was water-free but corrosive. The quantity of material to be transported would be reduced by over 80 per cent. The question was whether the risk to the public from the transport of the hazardous chemical was so low that it should be accepted, bearing in mind that a safer, though bulkier, material could be transported instead. It was assumed that the chemical could be carried in high-quality vehicles by well-trained drivers.

Calculations using average figures for the number of people killed in ordinary road accidents and in accidents involving chemicals showed that reducing the volume of material to be transported by 80 per cent would, on average, save one life every 12 years, even allowing for the fact than an accident involving a tanker of corrosive chemicals is very slightly more likely to result in a fatality than an accident involving a tanker of harmless material.

After Flixborough a BBC reporter, standing in front of the plant, described the explosion as 'the price of nylon'. Many people must have wondered if it is worth taking risks with men's lives so that we can have better shirts and underclothes. However, in our climate we have to wear something. How does the 'fatal accident content' of wool or cotton clothes compare with that of clothes made from synthetic fibres? The former is certainly higher. The price of any article is the price of the labour used to make it, capital costs being other people's labour. Agriculture is a low wage industry so there will be more hours of labour in a wool or cotton shirt than in a synthetic fibre shirt of the same price. And agriculture is a high accident industry; so there will be more fatal accidents in a wool or cotton shirt than in a nylon shirt.

In general, the newer technologies are safer than the old. Nuclear electricity claims fewer lives than electricity made from coal; plastic goods 'contain' fewer accidents than similar articles made from iron or wood.

3.4.9 RISKS TO THE ENVIRONMENT

Increasingly, companies are having to consider risks to the environment as well as risks to people. A number of attempts have been made to apply cost-benefit analysis to environmental risks — that is, to compare the costs of pollution with the costs of prevention (for example, References 38 and 53). The latter are comparatively easy to estimate. Some of the costs of pollution can also be estimated; for example, the costs of cleaning, corrosion and sound insulation.

We can also estimate the amount people are willing to pay in extra travel and housing costs to avoid living in polluted areas. It is much more difficult to put a price on the intangibles, such as the aesthetic value of pleasant surroundings or the desire to preserve as much as possible of the natural world and the evidence of the past. As with the value of a life (Section 3.4.7), their value is whatever we are prepared to pay to preserve them; it can be estimated by subtracting all the tangible benefits from the cost of prevention and seeing what is left. As with the value of life, the calculation is rarely made. People want the benefits and would rather not know the price, unaware that they are paying it. In a world in which many people are still suffering malnutrition and preventable disease, the value of some expenditure on improving the environment may be doubted. We should at least know what it is costing and what else could be done with the money.

3.5 ESTIMATING HOW OFTEN AN INCIDENT WILL OCCUR

As already mentioned, the methods described in this Section are used when we cannot use past experience.

3.5.1 SOME DEFINITIONS

HAZARD (OR INCIDENT) RATE *(H)* — The rate (occasions/year) at which hazards occur; for example, the rate at which the pressure in a vessel exceeds the design pressure or the rate at which the level in a tank gets too high and the tank overflows.

PROTECTIVE SYSTEM — A device installed to prevent the hazard occurring; for example, a relief valve or a high level trip.

TEST INTERVAL *(T)* — Protective systems should be tested at regular intervals to see if they are inactive or 'dead'. The time between successive tests is the test interval.

DEMAND RATE *(D)* — The rate (occasions/year) at which a protective system is called on to act; for example, the rate at which the pressure rises to the relief valve set pressure or the rate at which a level rises to the set point of the high level trip. 'Demand' is used in the French sense (demander = to ask).

FAILURE RATE *(f)* — The rate (occasions/year) at which a protective system develops faults. The faults of most interest to us are fail-danger faults which prevent the protective system operating, but fail-safe faults can also occur; these result in the protective system operating when it should not; for example, a relief valve lifts below its set pressure or a high level trip operates when the level is normal (see Section 3.5.10).

Most failures are random and this is assumed in what follows. However, failures can be high when equipment is new and when it is worn out (that is, just after birth and during old age).

FRACTIONAL DEAD TIME (fdt) — The fraction of the time that a protective system is inactive. This means it is the non-availability or the probability that it will fail to operate when required (fdt = 1 – availability).

If the protective system never failed to operate when required, then the hazard rate *(H)* would be 0. If there were no protective system then the hazard rate would be equal to the demand rate *(D)*. Usually the protective system is inoperative or dead for a (small) fraction of the time.

A hazard results when a demand occurs during a dead period, hence:

$H = D \times \text{fdt}$ (but see Section 3.5.6).

For other definitions see Reference 33.

Some of the figures used in the following examples are typical while others are merely examples.

3.5.2 EXAMPLE 1 — RELIEF VALVES

The failure of some equipment is obvious and is soon noticed by the operators. Relief valves and trips, however, are normally not operating and their failures remain unrevealed until a demand occurs. Hence we have to test them regularly to detect failures.

Tests on relief valves show that fail-danger faults which will prevent them lifting within 20% of the set pressure occur at a rate *(f)* of 0.01/year (once in 100 years — a typical figure).

Let test interval $T = 1$ year (a typical figure).

Failure occurs on average half-way between tests. Therefore the relief valve is dead for 6 months ($\frac{1}{2} T$) every 100 ($1/f$) years or for 1/200 or 0.005 of the time ($\frac{1}{2} fT$). This is the fractional dead time. Suppose the demand rate D is 1/year (an example). A hazard results when a demand occurs during the time that the relief valve is dead. The relief valve is dead for 1/200 of the time, there is one demand per year, so there is a hazard once in 200 years.

Expressed more precisely:

$$\begin{aligned}
\text{Hazard rate} &= \text{Demand rate} \times \text{fractional dead time} \\
&= D \times \tfrac{1}{2} fT \\
&= 1 \times 0.005 \\
&= 0.005/\text{year}
\end{aligned}$$

or once in 200 years. (The more accurate formula in Section 3.5.6 gives once in 250 years.)

We could not determine this figure by counting the number of occasions on which vessels have been overpressured because this occurs so rarely, but we have been able to estimate it from the results of tests on relief valves.

Note that in this example a hazard is defined as taking a vessel more than 20% above its design pressure. Not all these 'hazards' will result in vessel rupture or even a leak.

Relief valve failures are discussed in detail by Maher *et al*[37].

3.5.3 EXAMPLE 2 — SIMPLE TRIPS

Assume that:

- Fail-danger faults develop at a rate f of once every two years, or 0.5/year (a typical figure), much more frequently than with relief valves.
- The test interval T is 1 week (0.02/year, rather frequent).
- The demand rate D is 1/year (an example).

Calculate the fractional dead time and the hazard rate.

Answer: The trip is dead for 3.5 days every two years,

therefore fractional dead time	$= \dfrac{3.5}{2 \times 365} = 0.005$
and hazard rate	$= 1 \times 0.005$
	$= 0.005$/year or 1 in 200 years.
With monthly testing, fractional dead time	$= 0.02$
and hazard rate	= 1 in 48 years.
With annual testing, fractional dead time	$= 0.25$
and hazard rate	= 1 in 4 years.

(The more accurate formula in Section 3.5.6 gives 1 in 5 years.)

If a trip is never tested, then after a few years the fractional dead time will probably be 1 — that is, the trip will be 'dead', and the hazard rate will be the same as the demand rate.

Some companies test 'critical' trips and alarms but not 'non-critical' ones. If a trip or alarm is so unimportant that it does not need to be tested, it is probably not needed. If its failure rate is 0.5/y then after 4 years the probability that it will be in working order is less than 10 per cent. (However, if an alarm is fitted to a control or indicating instrument, certain failures, such as a failure of the sensor, may be obvious to the operators and it will then be repaired.)

If the trip is tested yearly, then the hazard rate is only reduced from once/year with no trip to once in 5 years. If the trip is so unimportant that annual testing is sufficient, then the trip is probably not necessary.

If we take into account the time the trip is dead while it is being tested, then weekly testing may not give the lowest hazard rate and monthly testing may be better. Because trips fail more often than relief valves they have to be tested more often.

3.5.4 EXAMPLE 3 — FREQUENT DEMANDS ON A TRIP

Let failure rate f = 0.5/year (as before)
test interval T = 0.1 year (5 weeks, a typical figure)
demand rate D = 100/year (much greater than before).

Calculate the fractional dead time and the hazard rate.

Answer: Using the formula

$$\text{Hazard rate} = D \times 0.5\, fT$$

$$\text{Hazard rate} = 100 \times 0.5 \times 0.5 \times 0.1 = 2.5/\text{year}.$$

In fact, the hazard will be almost the same as the failure rate (0.5/year) because:

- there will always be a demand in the dead period;
- the fault will then be disclosed and repaired.

2.5/year would be the right answer if, when a hazard occurred, we did not repair the trip but left it in a failed state until the next test was due.

Testing in this situation is a waste of time as almost all failures are followed by a demand before the next test is due. If you find this example hard to follow, consider the brakes on a car.

3.5.5 BRAKES ON CARS — ANOTHER EXAMPLE OF FREQUENT DEMANDS ON A TRIP

Let failure rate f = 0.1/year (a typical figure?)
test interval T = 1 year (as required by law)
demand rate D = 10^4/year (a guess).

Using the formula

$$\text{Hazard rate} = D \times 0.5\, fT = 10^4 \times 0.5 \times 0.1 \times 1 = 500/\text{year!}$$

Not even the worst drivers have this many accidents. The true answer is 0.1/year (why?).

These two examples show how we can get absurd answers if we substitute figures in a formula (or computer program) without understanding the reality behind them. For another example see Reference 39. So the simple intuitive formula that we derived in Section 3.5.1:

Hazard rate = demand rate × fractional dead time

must be incorrect.

3.5.6 A MORE ACCURATE FORMULA

Hazard rate = $f(1 - e^{-DT/2})$

where f = failure rate

T = test interval

D = demand rate

If $DT/2$ is small, this becomes

Hazard rate = $0.5\, fDT$

If $DT/2$ is large, this becomes

Hazard rate = f

The exponential formula above is correct only when fT is small and applies only to a single protective system.

For n identical systems, all tested at the same time,

$$\text{Hazard rate} = f^n T^{n-1} \left(1 - \exp\left[-\frac{DT}{n+1}\right]\right)$$

when fT is small.

The applicability of the two equations can be understood by looking at Figure 3.4 which shows the relationship between the hazard rate H and demand rate D.

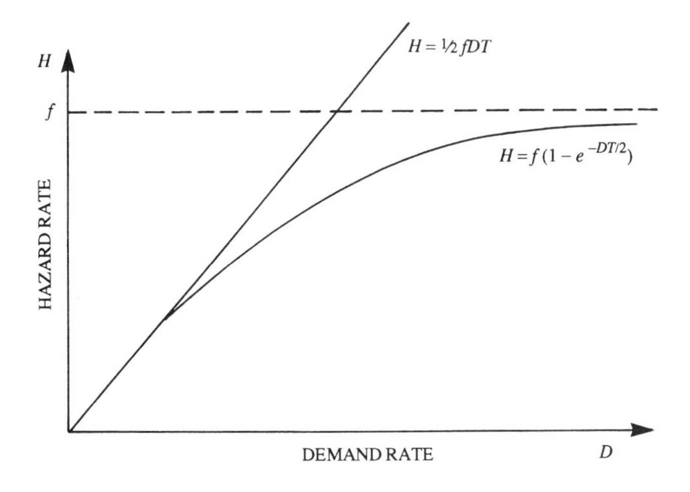

Figure 3.4 The relationship between hazard rate and demand rate.

TABLE 3.4
Dependence of hazard rate on test interval and demand rate

D per year	DT	$H = \frac{1}{2} fDT$ per year	$H = f(1 - e^{-DT/2})$ per year
0.1	0.2	0.001	0.00095
0.2	0.4	0.002	0.0018
0.4	0.8	0.004	0.0033
0.5	1.0	0.005	0.0039
1.0	2.0	0.01	0.0063
5.0	10.0	0.05	0.0099
10.0	20.0	0.1	0.01

When $DT = 1$ the difference between the two values of H is only about 25% but for higher values of DT the difference increases very quickly.

Table 3.4 shows how the method used for calculating H becomes increasingly important as DT rises. The figures apply to a relief valve; the failure rate f is assumed to be 0.01/year and the test interval T is assumed to be 2 years.

3.5.7 TWO PROTECTIVE SYSTEMS IN PARALLEL

Examples are two 100% relief valves in parallel or two high level trips (see Figure 3.5).

Let F_A, F_B be the fractional dead times of systems A and B. The set points of the two systems are, by accident or design, never exactly the same. Assume A responds first — that is, if A and B are two relief valves, A is set at a slightly lower pressure; if A and B are two high level trips, A is set at a lower level.

The demand rate on A = D.

The frequency of demands to which A does not respond is $F_A D$.

This is the demand rate on B.

Therefore it seems at first sight that the fractional dead time of the combined system should be $F_A F_B$ and the hazard rate should be $D F_A F_B$.

Actually the fractional dead time is $\frac{4}{3} F_A F_B$ and the hazard rate is $\frac{4}{3} D F_A F_B$ because the demands on B tend to occur towards the end of a proof test interval when there is a more-than-average likelihood that B will have failed.

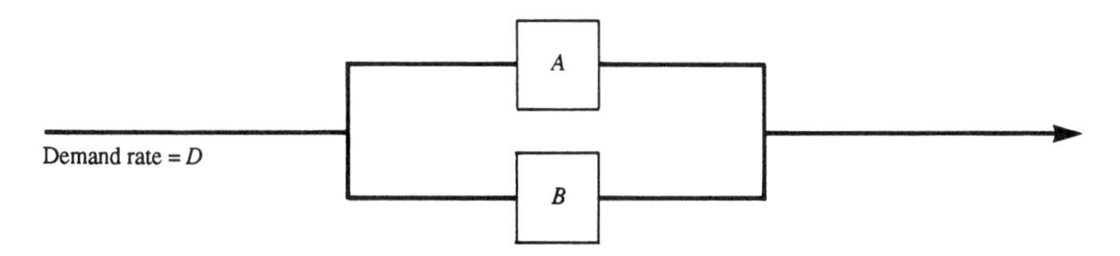

Figure 3.5 Two protective systems in parallel.

Figure 3.6 Two protective systems in series.

If A and B are tested at different times the hazard rate can be shown to be 0.83 $D\ F_A F_B$[40].

Like the example in Section 3.5.4, this shows the perils of intuitive mathematics. For another example of non-random demands see Section 3.6.7.

3.5.8 TWO PROTECTIVE SYSTEMS IN SERIES

An example is a relief valve and a bursting disc in series (Figure 3.6). ('Failure' of a bursting disc in this context means failure to burst when the required bursting pressure is reached.)

If A or B fails the system is dead.

Fdt of the whole system = $F_A + F_B - F_A F_B$

or $F_A + F_B$, if F_A, F_B are small.

If we connect in series many items of equipment each of which has a high reliability — that is, a low fractional dead time — the overall system may be very unreliable. For example, if there are ten items and each has an fdt of 0.05, the overall fdt will be about 0.4.

3.5.9 FAULT TREES

Fault trees are widely used in hazard analysis to set down in a logical way the events leading to a hazardous occurrence. They allow us to see the various combinations of events that are needed and the various ways in which the chain of events can be broken. They allow us to calculate the probability of the

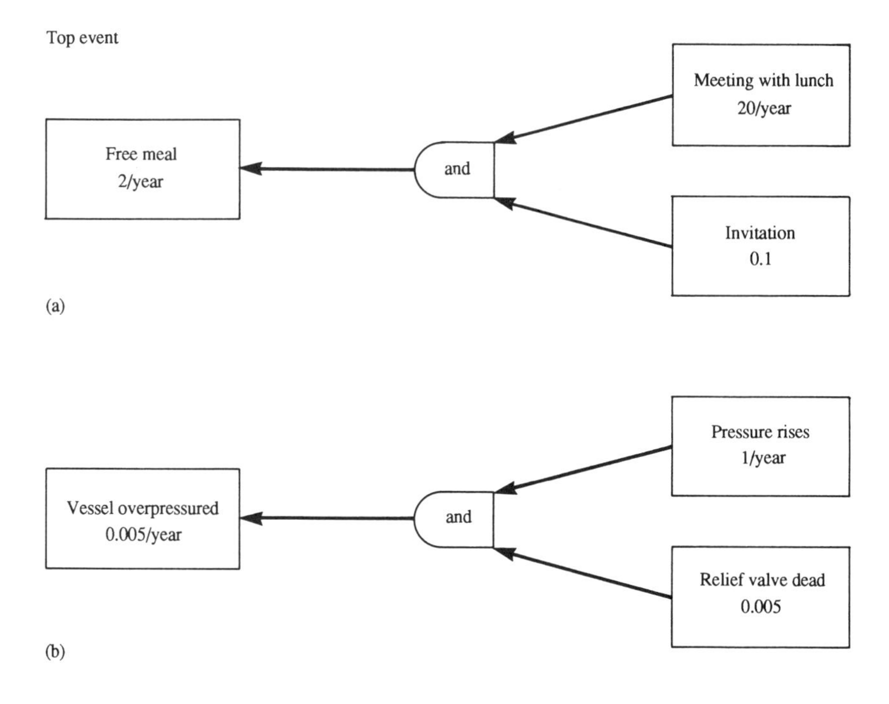

Figure 3.7 Fault trees with 'AND' gates. Note that a *frequency* is multiplied by a *probability*.

hazardous event from other probabilities that are known. Some examples of fault trees are shown in Figures 3.7 and 3.8.

In drawing a fault tree we start on the left with the hazardous event; for example, that common industrial hazard a free meal* (the logic is the same if you regard it as a desirable event) or the overpressuring of a vessel. Some people start at the top instead of the left so the hazardous event is often called the top event. We then work from left to right (or top to bottom) drawing in the various events that lead up to the top event. Then we work back inserting numbers and estimate the frequency of the top event.

The points at which two branches of a tree join are known as gates; they can be 'AND' or 'OR' gates.

---

* Not a problem in universities.

Figure 3.7 shows two examples of 'AND' gates. Both a meeting with lunch AND an invitation are required for a free meal. Note that a frequency is multiplied by a probability. A common beginner's mistake is to multiply two frequencies. Two or more probabilities *can* be multiplied together (as in Section 3.5.7).

In Figure 3.8 the logic trees have been extended and 'OR' gates are shown. We need visitors or a training course but not both to get a free meal. Note that at an 'OR' gate the two rates are added (or two or more probabilities as in Section 3.5.8).

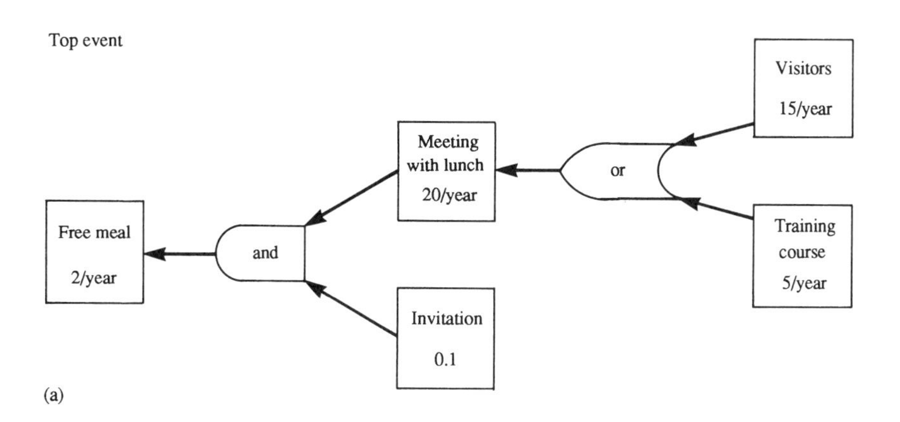

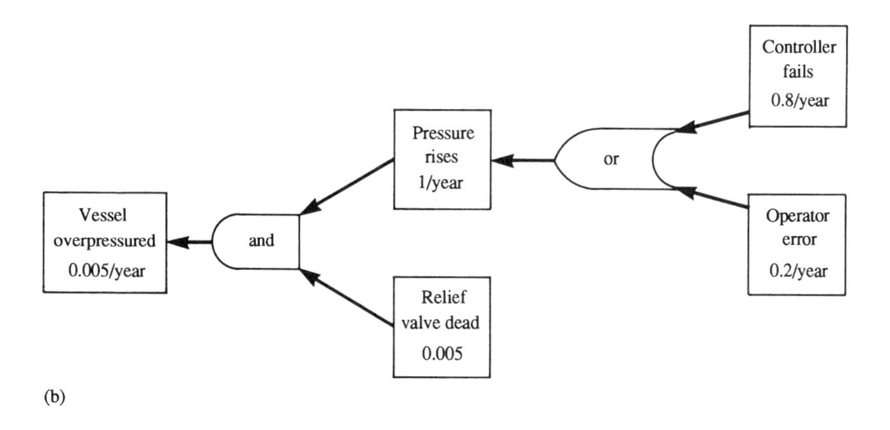

Figure 3.8 Fault trees with 'AND' and 'OR' gates. Note that *frequencies* are added at the 'OR' gates.

In practice we stop drawing when we have data for the frequency of the events or the probability of the conditions on the right (or the bottom) of the tree.

Suppose we are asked to revise Figure 3.8(a). We examine records for 10 years, carry out a regression analysis, allow for the effect of the changing economic situation and conclude that the visitor rate is more likely to be 12/y or 20/y instead of 15/y. The effect on the frequency of the top event is negligible. Similarly, detailed study may show that instead of 5 training courses per year we should expect 3, or perhaps 8. Again, the effect on the final answer is small. The number of free meals is between 1.5 and 2.8/y and is unlikely to be near these limits.

A more serious source of error is that we have overlooked the fact that some visitors may stay to dinner. If half of them do and the probability of an invitation is the same, the free meal rate rises to 2.75/y.

More serious still, suppose a new boss decides that all the staff should meet together over a free lunch once per week for an informal discussion. The free meal rate rises to 48/y (assuming 4 weeks holiday) + 2/y from other causes = 50/y. Our original result is out by a factor of 25!

This simple example shows that most errors in hazard analysis are not due to errors in the data but to errors in drawing the fault tree, to a failure to foresee all the hazards or all the ways in which the hazard could arise. Time is usually better spent looking for all the hazards and all the sources of hazard than in quantifying with ever greater precision those we have already found. There is another example of an unforeseen error in Section 4.4.

In Figures 3.7 and 3.8 we assumed that the probability of being invited to lunch is the same for the two sorts of lunch. This may not be so. In Figure 3.9, Figure 3.8(a) has been redrawn to allow for the fact that the probability of being invited to lunch with visitors may be different to the probability of being invited to lunch with a training course.

An industrial equivalent might be that the probability that an operator will take the correct action when an alarm sounds is not fixed, but differs for different alarms. Some alarms might be more noticeable or he might be trained to pay more attention to them.

It may be useful to summarise what has been said about 'AND' and 'OR' gates. At school we were taught that:

- AND means add.

Remember that in drawing logic trees:

- OR means add;
- AND means multiply (as in probability calculations).

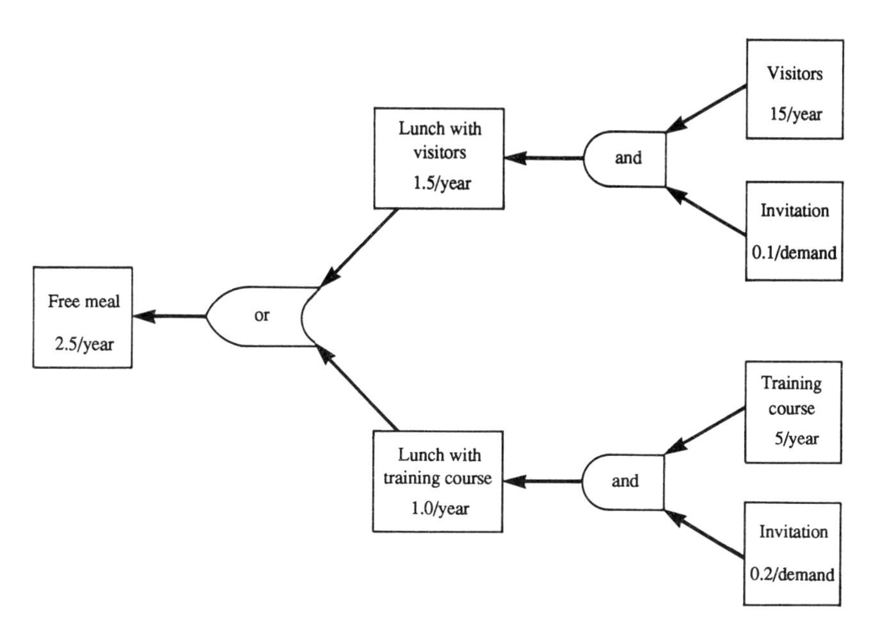

Figure 3.9 Figure 3.8(a) redrawn to show different probabilities on different branches.

As already stated, estimating hazard rates is not the only use of fault trees. They help us think out all the ways in which the hazard can arise and they show us which branches of the tree contribute the most towards the hazard rate. They show us how we can reduce the hazard rate and which methods will be most effective. For example, in the case of the free meal, we can reduce the hazard rate, the number of free meals per year, by reducing the number of visitors or the number of training courses or by reducing the probability that we shall be invited. We also see that halving the number of visitors will be more effective than halving the number of training courses.

To prevent confusion between rates and probabilities, always enter the units when drawing fault trees. If we are not clear whether the figure for the top event is a rate or a probability we cannot draw the tree correctly. The first time Figure 3.8(a) was published the editor thought that '/year' had been omitted from the 'Invitation' box in error, as it appeared in every other box, so he inserted it! Some authors suggest that we should write '/demand' after fractional dead times, as I have done in Figure 3.9.

Confusion over units is a common mistake in hazard analysis as a whole, not just in drawing fault trees. I consider this further in Section 4.2.

Another common error is confusing rates and duration. In one of the Andy Capp cartoons the eponymous hero was asked if it rained during a week he spent in the Lake District. He said it rained twice, 'Once for three days and once for four days'. The rate was low, twice per week, but the fractional dead time for dry weather was 100 per cent.

As an exercise draw a fault tree for 'car fails to start'.

Many people produce fault trees like Figure 3.10. A better one is shown in Figure 3.11. The need to take human failures into account as well as equipment failures is discussed further in Section 3.7.

3.5.10 REDUNDANCY AND VOTING SYSTEMS

As well as fail-danger faults, there are the so-called fail-safe faults or spurious trips — the protective equipment operates although there is no hazard. For example, a relief valve lifts light or a high level trip operates when the level is normal. I say 'so-called' because they may be unsafe in other ways; they may result in a discharge to atmosphere or an unnecessary plant shut-down. They give protective systems a bad name and make them unpopular with plant operators who may be tempted to by-pass them.

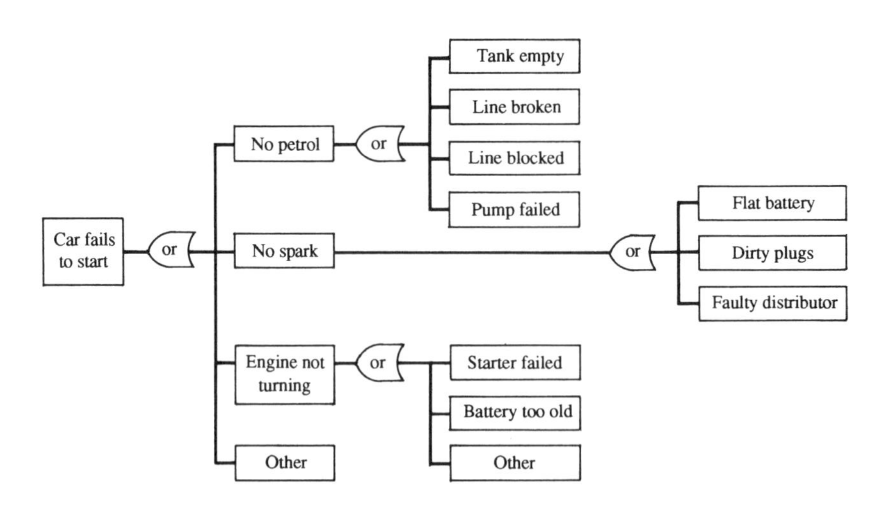

Figure 3.10 Fault tree for 'car fails to start'.

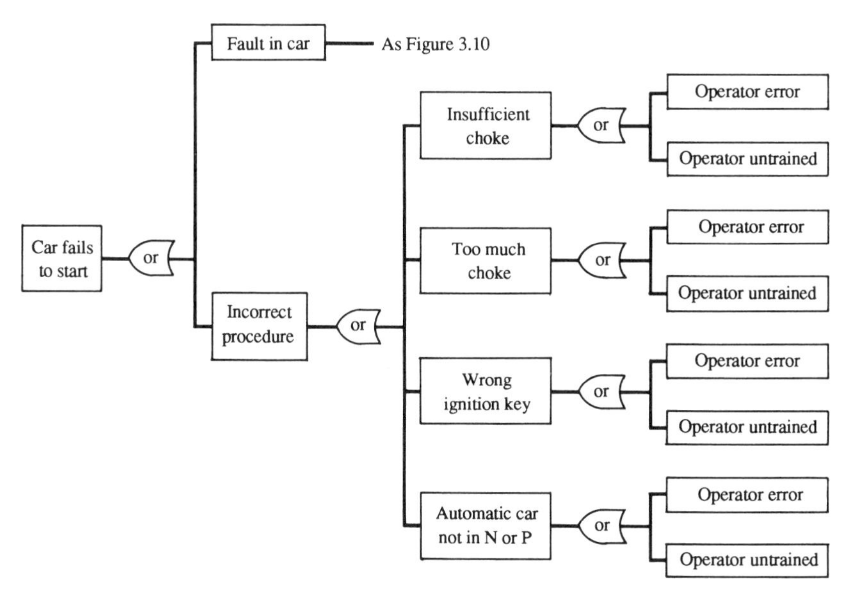

Figure 3.11 Revised fault tree for 'car fails to start'.

Table 3.5 shows how the fractional dead time depends on the fail-danger fault rate *(f)* and fail-safe fault rate *(S)* when there is some duplication of the protective system. This is called *redundancy* if the protective systems are the same or *diversity* if they are different. For example, two level measuring devices on a tank is an example of redundancy while a level measuring device combined with a device for measuring the weight of liquid in the tank is an example of diversity.

TABLE 3.5
Hazard rates for various combinations of protective systems

	Faults/year **Fail-safe**	**Fail-danger**	**Fractional dead time (simultaneous testing)**
1-out-of-1	S	f	$\frac{1}{2} fT$
1-out-of-2	$2S$	$f^2 T$	$\frac{1}{3} f^2 T^2$
1-out-of-3	$3S$	$f^3 T^2$	$\frac{1}{4} f^3 T^3$
2-out-of-3	$3S^2 T$	$3f^2 T$	$f^2 T^2$

Section 3.5.7 explained why the fractional dead time of a 1-out-of-2 system is $\frac{1}{3} f^2T^2$ and not $\frac{1}{2} fT \times \frac{1}{2} fT = \frac{1}{4} f^2T^2$. Similar arguments apply to the other systems[40].

In a 1-out-of-2 system the trip operates if either of two devices indicates a hazard — for example, a high level. A 1-out-of-3 system is similar. The whole trip, including the valve, may be duplicated (or triplicated) but often only the measuring instrument is duplicated (or triplicated).

A 2-out-of-3 system (last line) is an example of a voting system. Two out of three measuring instruments have to indicate a hazard before the trip operates. Only the measuring instruments are 2-out-of-3, not the valve. The valve may, of course, be duplicated (or even triplicated) if this is necessary to achieve the required reliability.

Voting reduces the fail-safe or spurious trip rate and is used when spurious trips would upset production. It does not give increased safety. A 1-out-of-2 system is three times safer than a 2-out-of-3 system.

It is helpful to remember that fail-safe faults are normally disclosed as soon as they occur. They result in a spurious trip. But fail-danger faults remain hidden until there is a test or demand. The formula $3S^2T$ for the fail-safe faults/year of a 2-out-of-3 system assumes that the faults are not disclosed. In practice, a single fault signal usually sounds an alarm and the fault is thereby disclosed. If this is the case, then instead of the test interval T the repair time should be used in the formula (or, more precisely, the time from the alarm sounding to the completion of the repairs).

Before installing voting systems to reduce spurious trips we should ask if the spurious trips are due to the inherent features of the instrumentation or to some other factors such as poor testing or maintenance. For example, in 1984 84 per cent of the trips on US nuclear power stations were spurious but half of them occurred on only 10 per cent of the plants; this suggests that standards on these plants were lower than on others. (In the worst incident several people were nearly drowned when water sprays, equivalent to 60 inches of rain per hour, operated inside a containment building[41].)

Rushton[50] has devised a systematic procedure for deciding which trip system configuration (1-out-of-1, 1-out-of-2, 2-out-of-3, etc) is most suitable for a particular application.

3.6 PITFALLS IN HAZARD ANALYSIS

So far the methods of hazard analysis appear straightforward. But a number of pitfalls await the unwary. Two have already been discussed in Sections 3.5.4 and 3.5.9. Others are discussed below. We start with data. Although errors in data, as shown in Section 3.5.9, are not the most important errors they nevertheless do occur and we should be on the lookout for them.

Chapter 6 gives some information on sources of data.

3.6.1 DATA MAY BE INAPPLICABLE

For example, published data on pumps may apply to different types, liquids, pressures, temperatures, corrosivities, etc. If we use the data without checking that conditions are similar, we may introduce serious errors. Leakage rates from flanged joints in a factory handling a corrosive chemical were found to be many times higher than in a factory handling clean petroleum liquids.

Instruments are similar wherever they are installed and their failure rates in different industries are unlikely to differ[7] by a factor of more than 3 or 4. This is not true of mechanical equipment. Sections 4.6 and 6.4 have more to say on this.

Note that a failure rate that is acceptable for one application may be quite unacceptable for another. A man drove 30 000 miles/year on business. His car broke down 3 times/year, usually far from home, so he discarded it as unreliable, bought another and gave the old one to his wife. She drove 3000 miles/year. The car broke down, near home, once in 3 years. She found it quite satisfactory.

3.6.2 DATA APPLY TO THE PAST

Designs change, and not necessarily for the better. For example, a component in an instrument might be made nowadays of aluminium alloy or plastic instead of steel. The manufacturer regards the change as trivial and does not tell his customers. But the new component fails more frequently or sooner than the old one.

A plant contained equipment to restart it automatically if power failed and was restored within 0.1 second. The manufacturer of the equipment, without telling anyone, changed the delay time to 1 second. This led to an explosion.

3.6.3 DATA AFFECTED BY MAINTENANCE POLICY

On beverage vending machines, for every 100 'demands':

- the RIGHT DRINK was obtained 94 times; and
- the WRONG DRINK was obtained 6 times.

Therefore the FAILURE RATE = 6%.

Before we assume that better machines are needed, let us see how the failure rate is made up. Wrong drink includes cold drinks, no drinks, short measures, etc. (We must always define what is meant by a failure.)

Figure 3.12

(a) Two of the failures in every 100 were due to the operator pressing the wrong button.

Therefore:

OPERATOR FAILURE RATE	= 2%
MACHINE FAILURE RATE	= 4%

Better mechanical reliability will therefore remove, at the most, two-thirds of the faults. To remove the others we would have to look at the factors which affect operator error (such as better layout of the panel, locating the machine where distraction is less, and so on).

(b) 98 demands in every 100 were made on machines in the office and there were 2 failures. The remaining 2 demands were made on machines in a local entertainment centre and every demand (2% of the total) resulted in a failure.

Therefore:

OPERATOR FAILURE RATE	= 2%
MACHINE FAILURE RATE — OFFICE	= 2%
MACHINE FAILURE RATE — ENTERTAINMENT CENTRE	= 100%

This shows that misleading results can be obtained if we group together widely differing data. For example, you can drown in a lake of average depth 6 inches (Figure 3.12).

A similar error was made by a politician who said, ' ... provisional laboratory identifications of *Salmonella* infections in humans amounted to 24 000 cases in 1988 ... other figures suggest that half of these were due to a strain associated with poultry and eggs' and went on to imply that action was therefore necessary to counter the infection in eggs[42]. However, many people believed that nearly all the infections were due to poultry. According to one estimate only one egg in 7000 was infected.

Similarly, the former Albanian dictator Enver Hoxha was quoted in the press[43] as saying, 'Together with the Chinese, the Albanians form one quarter of the world's population'.

(c) One failure was due to a broken cup.

Therefore:

OPERATOR FAILURE RATE	= 2%
FAILURE RATE DUE TO RAW MATERIAL QUALITY	= 1%
MACHINE FAILURE RATE — OFFICE	= 1%
MACHINE FAILURE RATE — ENTERTAINMENT CENTRE	= 100%

We now see that a more reliable machine would reduce the failure rate by only 1%. We could do as well by buying better cups or perhaps by redesigning the panel to reduce operator error.

Are the machines at the entertainment centre of a type that are more liable to break down or is the management — the system for reporting and repairing faults — different? Perhaps the users treat the machines differently.

Here is a more technical example of the way in which data can be affected by maintenance policy. Bellows were found to fail at a rate of 1 in 50 per year. Most of the failures did not result in large leaks but they caused shutdowns and loss of production. The failure rate seems high. Do we need a better product?

Analysis of the failures showed that some were due to specifying the wrong material of construction but most were due to poor installation. The failure rate does not give us information about bellows but information about the engineers who specify and install them. Data on the failure rate of mechanical equipment is often really data on the failure rate of people (see Section 6.4).

If we wish to reduce the failure rate we should:

- specify material of construction correctly;
- take more care over installation.

The first should not be difficult but the second is difficult. In practice bellows should be avoided when possible (by building expansion bends into the pipe-work) and more care taken over the installation of those we have.

A man had three Ford cars and crashed each of them, so he decided to try another make. Does this tell us something about Ford cars or about the man?

3.6.4 THE IMPOSSIBLY LOW FRACTIONAL DEAD TIME

Consider a 1-out-of-3 trip system.

Assume that the fractional dead time of each system = 10^{-2}

Then the fractional dead time of the total system = $2 \times (10^{-2})^3$

= 2×10^{-6}

(that is, 1 minute per year).

It would be 10^{-6} if testing were staggered (see Section 3.5.7).

Do we really believe that our instrument engineers can provide us with a protective system that is dead for only 1 minute per year? This calculation is wrong as it ignores two factors:

(a) The time the trips are out of action for testing;

(b) Common mode failures. For example, all three instruments are from the same manufacturer's batch and have a common manufacturing fault, all three instruments are affected by contaminants in the instrument air or process stream, all three impulse lines are affected by mechanical damage or flooding of a duct, or all three instruments are maintained by the same man who makes the same error. Two or three protective systems are never completely independent.

Therefore, we assume that the fractional dead time of a redundant system is never less than 10^{-4} (that is, 1 hour per year) and is often only 10^{-3} (that is, 10 hours per year). As we can get 10^{-4} with two trips, a third trip is not worth installing (except as part of a voting system).

For example, wearing a second pair of braces attached to the same buttons may reduce the chance of our trousers falling down. Failure of the buttons (the common mode) is now the biggest cause of failure and adding a third pair of braces, attached to the same buttons, will make no further improvement.

With a diverse system (that is, one in which the approach to a hazardous condition is measured in different ways — say by a change in an analysis, a change in pressure and a change in temperature), 10^{-5} (6 minutes per year) may be possible[44]. For example, belt and braces are better than two pairs of braces. This example illustrates the perils of using thorough mathematics and ignoring practicalities.

Another example of a common mode failure is shown in Figure 3.13(a), (b) and (c). A pressure switch installed on a firewater main switches on a pump when the pressure falls. The failure rate f is 0.8/year, the test interval T is 0.1 year and the demand rate D is 10/year. The hazard rate H, the frequency with which the pump fails to start on demand,

$= D \times 0.5\,fT$

$= 10 \times 0.5 \times 0.8 \times 0.1$

$= 0.4$/year or once in 2.5 years

or once in 3.2 years if we use the more accurate formula in Section 3.5.6.

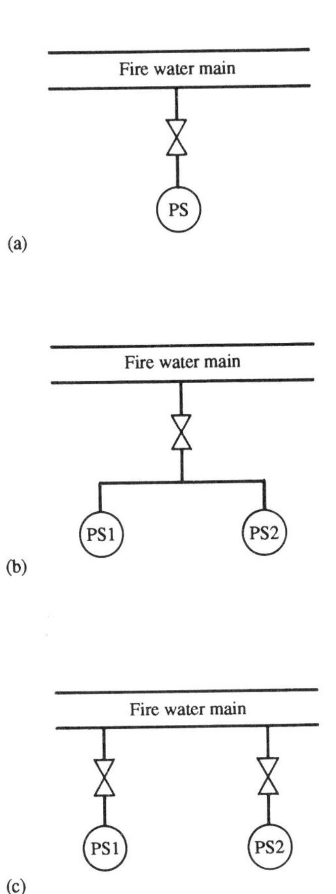

Figure 3.13 A common mode failure; (b) is little more reliable than (a), (c) is better.

The system shown in (b) was therefore installed. The hazard rate fell to only once in 4 years as the most likely reason for failure of the pressure switch is choking of the impulse line. The system shown in (c) has a hazard rate of once in 77 years.

3.6.5 MORE ABOUT COMMON MODE FAILURES

What is wrong with the trip system shown in Figure 3.14 on page 90?

The pressure in the vessel is measured by the pressure transmitter (PT) and controlled by the pressure indicator controller (PIC) which adjusts the setting on the motor valve. If this control system fails to work and the pressure rises above the set point, then the high pressure switch and trip (PSZ^{Hi}) operate to close the motor valve. At the same time the high pressure alarm (PA^{Hi}) operates.

This trip system is almost useless. The most likely causes of the pressure in the vessel getting too high are:

(1) Failure of the pressure transmitter (PT) or choking of the impulse line. If either occurs the trip will not know there is a high pressure in the vessel.

(2) Motor valve sticks open. In this case the trip will know that there is a high pressure in the vessel and will send a signal to the motor valve, but the motor valve will not respond.

(3) Failure of the pressure indicator (PIC). In this case the trip will work.

(3) is less likely than (1) or (2) as the PIC is in the clean atmosphere of the control room while the PT and valve are out on the plant. The trip will therefore operate on less than one third of the occasions when we want it to operate. Such a trip is not worth having. It is neither 'nowt nor summat'. It may do more harm than good, as we may expect it to operate and not watch the pressure so closely.

The system shown in Figure 3.15 has a high reliability. The high pressure trip and alarm ($PSZA^{Hi}$) has an independent connection to the vessel and operates a separate motor valve. There is a cross connection to the control valve. A high pressure switch (PS^{Hi}) and pre-alarm (PA^{Hi}) give a warning that

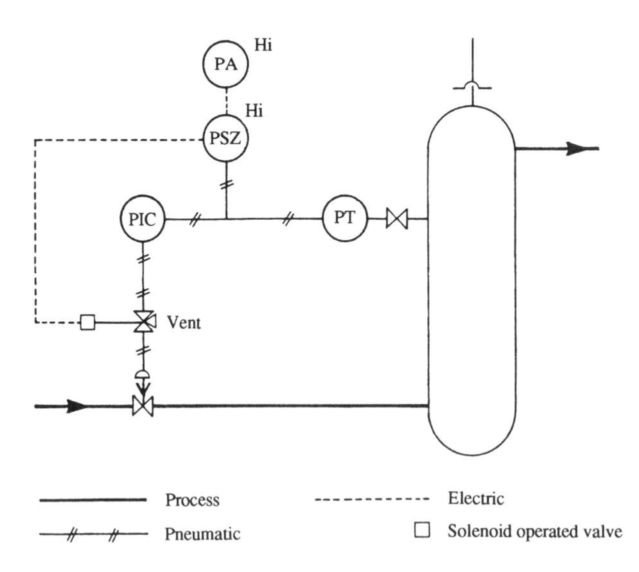

Figure 3.14 Original trip system.

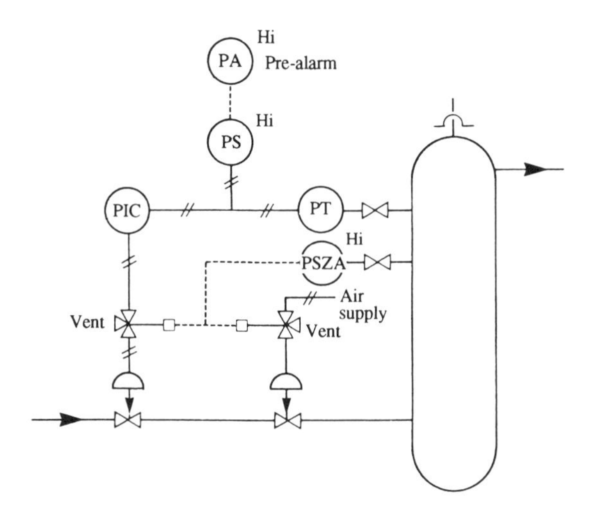

Figure 3.15 Modified trip system.

the pressure is approaching the trip setting and allow the operator to take action. This pre-alarm will operate if the rise in pressure is due to failure of the pressure indicator controller (PIC) or motor valve but not if it is due to failure of the pressure transmitter (PT). If a high pressure occurs the pre-alarm will operate on about two occasions out of three and the trip on almost all occasions.

The system shown in Figure 3.15 is expensive. That shown in Figure 3.14 may have been a compromise between no trip and the design shown in Figure 3.15, but it is a compromise that is worse than either extreme.

Another example of common mode failure: a group of chemical factories believed that power failure was impossible as their supply was duplicated. They did not realise that both supplies came from the same 132 kV overhead power lines. A fire in a warehouse underneath the power lines caused a complete loss of power and several incidents in the chemical factories, including a fire[51].

3.6.6 DESIGNER'S INTENTIONS NOT FOLLOWED

The tank shown in Figure 3.16 (see page 92) was filled once/day. Originally the operator switched off the pump when the tank was full. After 5 years the inevitable happened. One day the operator allowed his attention to wander and the tank was overfilled. A high-level trip was then installed. To everyone's surprise, the tank was overfilled again after 1 year.

The trip had been used as a process controller to switch off the pump when the level rose to the set point. The operator no longer watched the level.

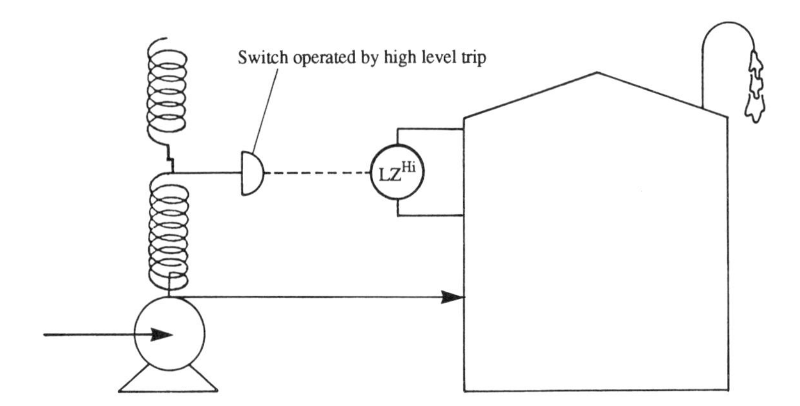

Figure 3.16 Tank fitted with high level trip.

The manager knew this and thought that better use was being made of the operator's time. When the trip failed, as it was bound to do after a year or two, another spillage occurred.

It is almost inevitable that the operator will use the trip in this way. We should either remove the trip and accept an occasional spillage or install two trips — one to function as a process controller and one to act when the controller fails. The single trip increased the probability of a spillage.

In this example and the last one we saw that no trip was a reasonable solution and so was a good trip. The compromise solution was a waste of money. On occasions either of two extremes makes sense but a compromise does not. (Because this is true of instrumentation do not assume it is true elsewhere.)

A similar incident occurred on a plant in which a delivery tank was filled frequently from a suction tank. To reduce effort, the operators switched off the pump between transfers but did not close any valves. They relied on a non-return valve to prevent reverse flow. Inevitably, one day the non-return valve failed (a piece of wire had become trapped in it), and reverse flow occurred from the delivery tank, backwards through the pump to the suction tank, which was overfilled.

3.6.7 NON-RANDOM FAILURES

A new plant had two 100% compressors (1 working, 1 spare). The failure rate and the time required for repair were known. Calculation showed that if failures are random, the off-line time would be 0.04% (3 hours per year). The actual off-line time was 1.8% (144 hours per year). Why?

The failure rates and repair times were as expected but the failures were not random; most occurred soon after a compressor had been put on line. This may have been due to wrong diagnosis of the fault, installation of wrong parts or incorrect re-assembly.

Mathematical techniques (Weibull analysis) for handling non-random failure are available if the need to use them is recognised[8].

Most machinery, perhaps all equipment with moving parts, seems to fail in a non-random way. One study showed that valve failure is due to wear[45]. Motor cars provide another example of non-random failure — they are more likely to require attention during the week after servicing than at any other time. If you had two cars (one working, one spare) and one had just been serviced, would you leave it unused until the other broke down or required servicing?

Non-random incidents can be due to non-random demands as well as non-random failures of equipment. A study showed that bank cash machines failed to operate when required on 17 per cent of the occasions on which they were used. The banks said that the non-availability of the machines was only half this figure. The banks quoted an average availability round the clock but the trials measured the availability at the time of use. Usage is heavy on Saturdays when there is usually no-one available to repair or refill the machines[46].

There is another example of non-random demands in Section 3.5.7.

3.7 THE MAN OR WOMAN IN THE MIDDLE

Figure 3.17 illustrates a common plant situation. When the alarm sounds the operator has to go outside and close a valve within, say, 10 minutes.

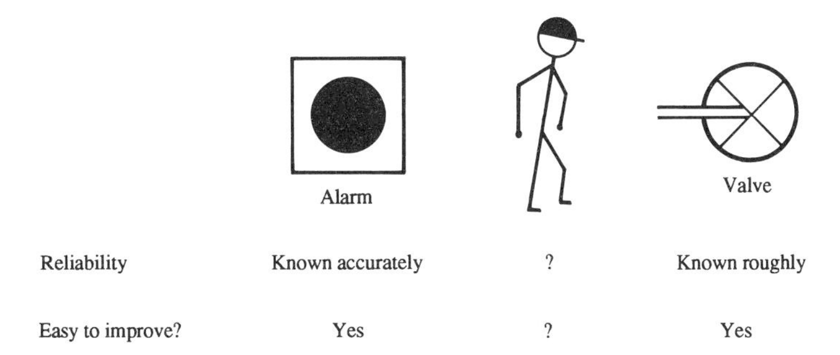

Figure 3.17 Reliabilities in a man/machine system.

The reliability of the alarm is known. If it is too low it is easy to improve it by adding redundancy or diversity — that is, by adding in parallel identical components or different components capable of performing the same function (see Section 3.5.10). The reliability of the valve is known roughly and if we do not think it is high enough we can use a better quality valve or two valves in series. But what about the reliability of the operator? Will he always close the right valve in the required time?

At one time people assumed he would — or should. If he did not he should be told to pay more attention. Other people have gone to the other extreme and said that sooner or later all operators make mistakes and therefore we need fully automatic equipment.

Both these extremes are unscientific. We should not say, 'The operator always should' or 'The operator never will' but ask *why* he does not always close the right valve in the required time and *how often* he will do so. The failure to close the valve in the required time may be due to lack of training or instructions (he does not know he should do so), to a deliberate decision not to do so, to lack of physical or mental ability or (and this is the most likely reason) to a momentary slip or lapse of attention. We cannot estimate the probability of the first three causes but we can perhaps assume that failures for these reasons will continue in an organisation at the same rate as in the past, unless there is evidence of change.

The probability of a slip or lapse of attention can be estimated roughly. The answer will depend on the degree of stress and distraction and the suggestions in Table 3.6 may help us make a judgement.

TABLE 3.6
Suggested human failure rates

1 in 1	When complex and rapid action is needed to avoid a serious incident. The operator will not really be as unreliable as this but he will be very unreliable and we should assume this figure and install fully automatic systems.
1 in 10	In a busy control room where other alarms are sounding, the telephone is ringing, people are asking for permits-to-work and so on.
1 in 100	In a quiet control room, for example, a storage area control room — if the man is present.
A figure between these last two may be estimated.	
1 in 1000	If the valve to be closed is immediately below the alarm.

In carrying out a familiar routine, such as starting up a batch reactor, a typical failure rate is 1 in 1000 *for each operation* (for example, close valve). Some of these failures will be immediately apparent but others will not[9].

Note that the figures in Table 3.6 assume that the operators are well trained, capable and willing. As already stated, it is impossible to give a figure for the probability that this assumption is correct; it can vary from 0 to 1 depending on the policy of the company. We can however make a rough estimate of the probability that a man will have a moment's aberration — as we all do in everyday life — and forget to carry out a prescribed task (see Section 4.7).

It must also be remembered that not all tasks can be prescribed. Sometimes the operator has to diagnose the correct action from the alarm and other instrument signals and may not do so correctly, particularly if the instruments are not reading correctly. This happened at Three Mile Island[10].

Finally, remember that installing a fully-automatic system does not remove our dependence on men. Instead of relying on the operator we are now dependent on the men who design, install, test and maintain the fully automatic equipment. They also make mistakes. They work under conditions of less stress so we may improve the overall reliability by installing fully-automatic systems but we should not kid ourselves that we have removed our dependence on men.

For a fuller discussion of human error see Reference 9.

3.8 EXAMPLES OF HAZARD ANALYSIS

3.8.1 A BETTER PROTECTIVE SYSTEM OR A BETTER MATERIAL OF CONSTRUCTION?

A plant[47] handled ethylene gas at –100°C. It was realised, after construction was complete, that instrument failure could result in the cold gas reaching some mild steel pipework. If it did, the pipework might fracture and the gas would then escape and might ignite. Two methods of protection were considered: replacing the mild steel by stainless steel at a considerable cost or improving the trip system at one quarter of the cost.

The improved trip system contained three independent layers of protection (see Figure 3.18 on page 96):

(1) A high level alarm on a catchpot;

(2) A high level trip, set at a higher level, which closed a valve on the inlet line to the catchpot;

(3) A low temperature trip on the gas exit line from the catchpot which closed a valve in the gas line. (The catchpot and overhead line were made from stainless steel but the line led to a mild steel line.)

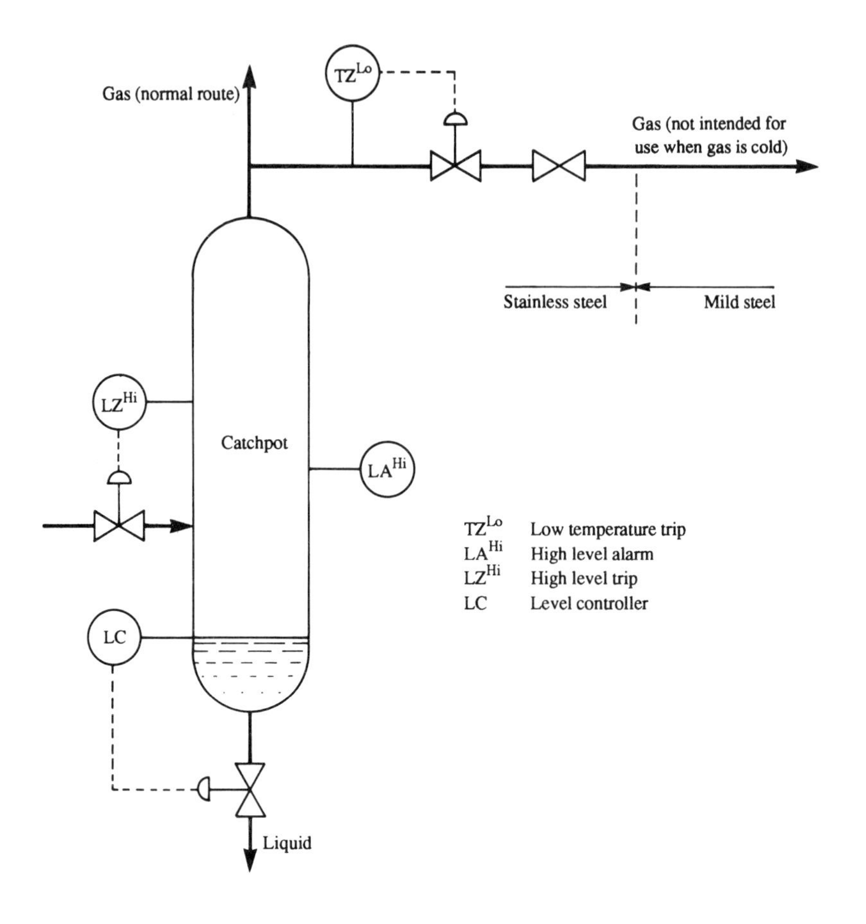

Figure 3.18 Protective system to prevent overcooling of mild steel pipeline.

The fractional dead time of the redesigned trip system was calculated from data on the reliability of the components and the test frequency. It was assumed that the operator would ignore the alarm on one quarter of the occasions on which it operated. The demand rate was estimated from experience on similar plants. The hazard rate, the frequency with which cold gas would contact the mild steel, was found to be once in 10 000 years or once in 2500 years for the whole plant which contained four similar systems.

It was assumed that on one tenth of the occasions on which the trip system failed there would be a leak and an explosion and the operator would be killed, almost certainly an overestimate. The operator will therefore be killed once in 25 000 years giving an FAR of 0.45 (see Section 3.4.2), close to the target of 0.4 for a single risk considered in isolation (see Section 3.4.1). It was therefore agreed that the protective system, as modified, was adequate, and that it was not necessary to replace the mild steel.

If the mild steel had been replaced, the already low risk would have been made even lower and the cost per life saved (see Section 3.4.7) would have been about £150M at 1970 prices (about £1250M at 1991 prices). This cost is a notional one — that is, spending the money would make an already low risk even lower but it is very unlikely that anyone will be killed if the money is not spent. In contrast, many of the costs of saving a life listed in Table 3.3 are not notional; real lives will be saved if more money is spent on health or road safety.

Note that the decision might have been different if the hazard had been identified during design. Unfortunately no hazop was carried out.

3.8.2 STOPPING A REACTION

A reactor (Figure 3.19) was fitted with a kill system[48]. If measurements showed that the reaction was getting out of control, the kill valve opened and a catalyst poison, stored under nitrogen pressure, was injected. To prevent the poison

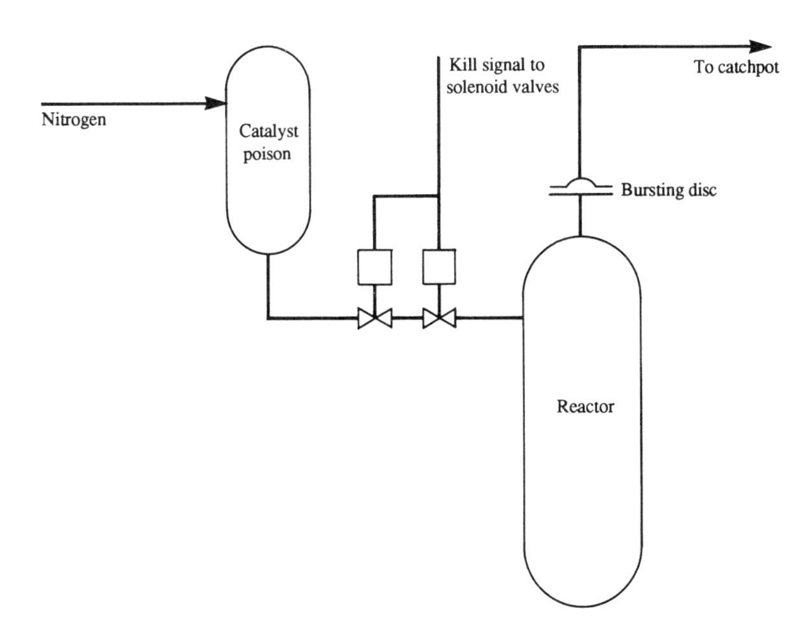

Figure 3.19 Reactor with kill system.

leaking into the reactor and to reduce the chance of spurious operation the kill valve was duplicated in series and both kill valves were 'fail closed'. The kill system could also be activated by the operator.

Originally, if the kill system failed to operate, a bursting disc, connected to a catchpot, would burst and prevent damage to the reactor. After a plant expansion the bursting disc was no longer big enough to prevent damage and it became necessary to improve the reliability of the kill system. Table 3.7 shows several cases that were considered. Case 2 was the existing system. It is seen that the kill system will be three times more reliable if the two 'fail closed' valves are replaced by a single 'fail open' valve (Case 4). If the site cooling water supply failed the operator had to activate the kill system and an allowance was made for the probability that he would fail to do so.

Installing two parallel kill valves (Case 5) makes only a slight improvement in reliability. If a hazard analysis had not been carried out, this option would probably have been adopted on the philosophy that 'if one is good, two must be better'. The hazard analysis showed that the least reliable component of the kill system was the solenoid valve that actuated the kill valve. Duplication of the solenoid valve gave almost the same reliability as Case 5.

TABLE 3.7
Comparison of reliability of kill system configurations

Case	Design option	Failure rate (freq/yr)	Probability of failure compared to Case 4
1	Single valve (fail closed)	1.6×10^{-2}	1.95
2	Series valves (fail closed)	2.6×10^{-2}	3.17
3	Single valve (fail open)	1.1×10^{-2}	1.34
4	Single valve (fail open) (operator action)	8.2×10^{-3}	1.0
5	Parallel valves (fail open) (operator action)	6.6×10^{-3}	0.8

3.8.3 INSET OR PARALLEL BERTHS FOR GAS TANKERS?

A company wanted to construct a berth alongside a river bank for loading liquefied gas. The port authority was concerned that while a ship was at the berth another ship, passing along the river, might get out of control and collide with the gas ship. They suggested that the berth should be located in a specially constructed inlet at right angles to the bank.

Few, if any, liquefied gas ships have been involved in collisions in harbours. The probability of a collision was therefore estimated from the frequency of collisions to other ships serious enough to have ruptured the tanks on a gas ship. This study showed that a collision between a ship and the bank, while it was manoeuvering into a confined space, was several times more likely than a collision between two ships while one was tied up at a berth. Constructing an inlet would have made a collision more, not less, probable. This conclusion was valid for the particular river but may not be true for other rivers.

At first sight constructing an inset berth seems an obvious way of increasing safety. Numerical treatment of the problem shows that the obvious solution actually increases the risk. The study also showed that the most effective way of reducing the probability of a collision is to prohibit the movement of ships in the opposite direction when a gas ship is moving.

3.8.4 BALANCING PROBABILITIES AND CONSEQUENCES

The risk of injury or damage depends on the size and probability of a leak. Is it more effective to reduce the size or reduce the probability? Hazard analysis may help us answer this question.

If the inventory in a plant or storage area is reduced the maximum size of a leak will be less and so the consequences will be less but the probability of a leak will not be changed. Reducing the number of leak points such as valves, drains, pumps, etc, may be more effective than reducing the inventory in the existing equipment. If, however, it is possible to take a vessel out of service then there will be fewer places from which leaks can occur and both the probability and maximum size of a leak will be lower[52].

3.8.5 OTHER EXAMPLES

Lawley[11,12,13] has described three hazard analyses in detail, showing fault trees and explaining the derivation of each item of data used. The first[11], which is quoted by *Lees*, Chapter 9, analyses the precautions taken to prevent a series of crystallisers overflowing, the second[12] analyses the precautions taken to prevent a pipeline getting so cold that it becomes brittle and might fail, and the third[13] analyses the precautions taken to prevent loss of level in the base of a distillation column and discharge of high pressure gas into a low pressure tank.

Reference 24 describes how the methods of hazard analysis have been applied to a number of high-technology industries.

The subject of this Chapter is discussed more fully in References 13–17 and in *Lees*, Chapter 9. References 16 and 17 deal particularly with risks to the public. Reference 17 reviews the various targets or criteria that have been proposed.

There is an enormous literature on the philosophy of risk acceptability, most of which deals with the more philosophical difficulties, and does not offer much advice to the practitioner. References 18–22 and 26 are typical of these publications while Reference 23 is somewhat more practical in its approach.

3.9 A SUMMARY OF THE MAIN SOURCES OF ERROR IN HAZARD ANALYSIS

(1) Failure to foresee all the hazards or all the ways in which a hazard can arise (see Section 3.5.9).

(2) Errors in the logic (see Sections 3.5.4 and 3.6.5).

(3) Failure to foresee that protection may not be fully effective because of poor design (see Section 3.6.4) or because time of action has been ignored.

(4) Design assumptions not correct; for example, less testing, more demands, failures not random (see Section 3.6.7), different mode of operation (see Section 3.6.6).

(5) Common mode failures (see Sections 3.6.4 and 3.6.5).

(6) Wrong data (see Sections 3.6.1–3.6.3).

Some other errors are discussed in Chapter 4.

3.10 A FINAL NOTE

To many people the calculations of this Chapter and others on the subject may seem coldblooded or even callous. Safety, like everything else, can be bought at a price. The more we spend on safety, the less we have with which to fight poverty and disease or to spend on those goods and services which make life worth living, for ourselves and others. Whatever money we make available for safety we should spend in such a way that it produces the maximum benefit. There is nothing humanitarian in spending lavishly to reduce a particular hazard which has been brought to our attention and ignoring the others.

Those who make the sort of calculations described in this Chapter, far from being coldblooded or callous, are the most effective humanitarians, as they allocate the resources available in a way which will produce the maximum benefit to their fellow men.

REFERENCES IN CHAPTER 3

1. ICI, 1968, *Assessing projects: Book 5, Risk analysis*, Methuen, London.
2. Kerridge, A.E., December 1982, *Hydrocarbon Processing*, 61 (12): 56.
3. Kletz, T.A., 1990, *Improving chemical industry practices —a new look at old myths of the chemical industry*, Hemisphere, New York, 5.
4. Kletz, T.A. and Lawley, H.G., 12 May 1975, *Chemical Engineering*, 81.
5. Gibson, S.B., February 1976, *Chemical Engineering Progress*, 72 (2): 59.
6. Lees, F.P., 1980, in *Proceedings of the Third International Symposium on Loss Prevention and Safety Promotion in the Process Industries*, Swiss Society of Chemical Industries, 6/426.
7. Lees, F.P., 1976, A review of instrument failure data, *Symposium Series No. 47*, Institution of Chemical Engineers, Rugby, UK, 73. See also *Lees*, Section 13.6.
8. Aird, R.J., 1980, Reliability assessment of pumps, *Convention on Fluid Machinery Failure,* Institution of Mechanical Engineers, London, paper C145/80. See also *Lees*, Chapter 7.
9. Kletz, T.A., 1991, *An engineer's view of human error*, 2nd edition, Institution of Chemical Engineers, Rugby, UK.
10. Kletz, T.A., 1988, *Learning from accidents in industry*, Butterworths, Tonbridge, UK, Chapter 11.
11. Lawley, H.G., April 1974, *Chemical Engineering Progress*, 70 (4): 45.
12. Lawley, H.G., October–December 1980, *Reliability Engineering*, 1 (2): 89.
13. Kletz, T.A. and Lawley, H.G., 1982, in *High risk safety technology*, edited by A.E. Green, Wiley, London, Chapter 2.1.
14. Kletz, T.A., May 1977, *Hydrocarbon Processing*, 56 (5): 297.
15. Kletz, T.A., October 1978, *Chemical Engineering Progress*, 74 (10): 47.
16. Kletz, T.A., 1976, in *Chemical Engineering in a Changing World, Proceedings of the World Congress of Chemical Engineering*, edited by W.T. Koetsier, Elsevier, Amsterdam, 397.
17. Kletz, T.A., July 1982, *Reliability Engineering*, 3 (4): 325.
18. Lowrance, W.W., 1976, *Of acceptable risk*, Kaufmann, Los Altos, California.
19. Council for Science and Society, 1975, *The acceptability of risks*, Rose, London.
20. The Royal Society, 1981, *The assessment and perception of risk*, London.
21. The Royal Society, 1983, *Risk assessment. A study group report*, London.
22. Schwing, R.C. and Albers, W.A. (editors), 1980, *Societal risk assessment*, Plenum Press, New York and London.
23. Griffiths, R.F. (editor), 1981, *Dealing with risk*, Manchester University Press.
24. Green, A.E. (editor), 1982, *High risk safety technology*, Wiley, London.
25. Pitblado, R.M., Shaw, S.J. and Stevens, G., 1990, The SAFETI risk assessment package and case study applications, *Symposium Series No. 120*, Institution of Chemical Engineers, Rugby, UK, 51.
26. *Risk analysis in the process industries —Report of the international study group on risk analysis*, 1985, Institution of Chemical Engineers, Rugby, UK.
27. Kletz, T.A., 1991, *Plant design for safety —a user-friendly approach*, Hemisphere, New York.

28. Mann, M., May 1986, *Journal of the Royal Society of Arts*, 134 (5358): 396.
29. Withers, J., 1988, *Major industrial hazards*, Gower, Aldershot, UK, 85–97.
30. Health and Safety Executive, 1989, *Risk criteria for land-use planning in the vicinity of major industrial hazards*, HMSO, London.
31. Barnes, M., 1988, *The Hinckley Point public inquiry: Report*, HMSO, London, Chapters 34 and 35.
32. Health and Safety Executive, 1988, *The tolerability of risk from nuclear power stations*, HMSO, London.
33. *Nomenclature for hazard and risk assessment in the process industries*, 1985, Institution of Chemical Engineers, Rugby, UK.
34. British Medical Association, 1987, *Living with risk*, Wiley, Chichester, UK.
35. *Risk communication, risk statistics and risk comparisons*, 1988, Chemical Manufacturers Association, Washington, DC.
36. Kletz, T.A., 1988, in *Engineering risk and hazard assessment*, edited by A. Kandel and E. Avni, CRC Press, Boca Raton, Florida, 11.
37. Maher, S.T. *et al*, 1988, Relief valve testing optimisation programme for the cost-effective control of major hazards, *Symposium Series No. 110*, Institution of Chemical Engineers, Rugby, UK, 117.
38. Programmes Analysis Unit, 1972, *An economic and technical appraisal of air pollution in the UK*, HMSO, London.
39. Kletz, T.A., 1990, *Improving chemical industry practices —a new look at old myths of the chemical industry*, Hemisphere, New York, 116.
40. *Lees*, Tables 13.17 and 13.18.
41. O'Mara, R.L. and Bergeron, C.B., 1987, Inherent safety — how to keep a new safety system from causing an accident, *American Institute of Chemical Engineers Annual Meeting, New York, 15–20 November 1987.*
42. Lloyd, T., March 1989, *The Chemical Engineer*, No. 458, 15.
43. Heffer, S., 1 June 1991, *The Daily Telegraph*, 15.
44. Stewart, R.M., 1971, High integrity protective systems, *Symposium Series No. 34*, Institution of Chemical Engineers, Rugby, UK, 99.
45. *Process News*, July 1989, Institution of Mechanical Engineers Process Industries Division, London, 8 (summary of paper by D. W. Heckle and Dr Young).
46. *Which?*, February 1991, 71.
47. Kletz, T.A., 1971, Hazard analysis — a quantitative approach to safety, *Symposium Series No. 34*, Institution of Chemical Engineers, Rugby, UK, 75.
48. French, R.W., Olsen, R.E. and Peloquin, G.L., February 1990, *Process Safety and Environmental Protection*, 68 (B1): 7.
49. Goyal, R.K. and Al-Jurashi, N.M., April 1991, *Journal of Loss Prevention in the Process Industries*, 4 (3): 151.
50. Rushton, A.G., November 1991, *Process Safety and Environmental Protection*, 69 (B4): 200.
51. Ratcliffe, K.B., April 1991, *Loss Prevention Bulletin*, No. 098, 21.
52. Schaler, L.C., January 1990, *Plant/Operations Progress*, 9 (1): 50.
53. Barde, J-P. and Pearce, D.W., 1991, *Valuing the environment*, Earthscan, London.

APPENDIX TO CHAPTER 3 — BELT AND BRACES

Here is a simple example of the application of numerical methods to safety problems, showing how a hazard can be reduced to any desired level but not eliminated completely.

The accident we wish to prevent is our trousers falling down and injuring our self-esteem. Braces are liable to break and the protection they give is not considered adequate. Assume that breakage through wear and tear is prevented by regular inspection and replacement and that we are concerned only with failure due to inherent weaknesses or faults in manufacture which cannot be detected beforehand and which are random events.

Experience shows that, on average, each pair of braces breaks after 10 years' service. Experience also shows that belts fail in the same way and as frequently as braces. Collapse of our trousers once in 10 years is not considered acceptable.

How often will a belt and braces fail together? If one fails then it will not be detected until the item is removed at the end of the day. Assuming it is worn for 16 hours per day, then, on average, every man is wearing a broken belt for eight hours every 10 years and broken braces for eight hours every 10 years.

The fractional dead time (fdt) of the braces is

$$\frac{8}{16} \times \frac{1}{10} \times \frac{1}{365} = 0.000137$$

and the fdt of the belt is the same.

The chance of the second protective device failing while the first one is 'dead' is:

$$\text{Hazard rate} = \text{Demand rate} \times \text{fdt}$$

$$= 2 \times \frac{1}{10} \times 0.000137 = 2.74 \times 10^{-5}/\text{year}$$

or once in 36 500 years.

Failure of belt and braces together, therefore, occurs once in 36 500 years. At the individual level this risk is acceptable. However, there are about 25 000 000 men in Great Britain so that, even if every man wears 'belt and braces', 685 men will lose their trousers every year. At the national level it is considered unacceptable that so many men should be embarrassed in this way.

To reduce the risk further, every man could wear a third protective device, a second pair of braces. This would reduce the failure rate for the individual man to once in 133 000 000 years* and for the country as a whole to once in 5 years. A third protective device, however, involves considerable extra capital expenditure and makes the system so complicated that people may fail to use it. An alternative is to get every man to inspect his belt and braces every two hours to see if either has broken. This will reduce the failure rate for the individual to once in 36 500 × 8 = 292 000 years and for the country as a whole to 685/8 = 85 men/year. This may be considered acceptable but is it possible to persuade men to inspect their 'protective systems' with the necessary regularity and what would it cost in education to persuade them to do so?

This example illustrates the following general points:

(1) The risk can be reduced to any desired level by duplication of protective equipment but it cannot be completely eliminated. Some slight risk always remains. Even with three protective devices it could happen that coincident failure occurs not after 133 000 000 years, but next year.

(2) The method used here is sound but the result is only as good as the input data. If the failure rate for belt or braces is not once in 10 years but once in five or twenty years, then the conclusion will be in error, not by a factor of two, but

---

* Coincident failure of belt and two pairs of braces can occur in three ways, namely:

(a) Belt fails when both pairs of braces have already failed;

(b) Braces 1 fail when belt and braces 2 have already failed;

(c) Braces 2 fail when belt and braces 1 have already failed.

The fdt for a 1-out-of-2-system is $\frac{1}{3} f^2 T^2$ (see Table 3.5)

where f = failure rate (0.1/year)

and T = test interval (1/365 year).

For each failure mode the hazard rate

$$= \text{demand rate} \times \text{fdt}$$

$$= 0.1 \times \tfrac{1}{3} f^2 T^2$$

Hence total hazard rate

$$= 3 \times 0.1 \times \tfrac{1}{3} f^2 T^2$$

$$0.1\left(\frac{0.1}{365}\right)^2$$

$$= 7.5 \times 10^{-9}/\text{year}$$

or once in 133 000 000 years.

The calculations are approximate as they do not make any allowance for common mode failures (see Sections 3.6.4 and 3.6.5).

by a factor of four for two protective devices and by a factor of eight for three protective devices.

(3) The event which we wish to prevent is not collapse of our trousers but injury to our self-esteem. Half (say) of the collapses will occur when we are alone or at home and will not matter, thus introducing an extra factor of two. (It is not explosions we wish to prevent but the damage and injury they cause; explosions which produce neither are acceptable.)

(4) A risk which is acceptable to an individual may not be acceptable to the community as a whole.

(5) It is easier to devise protective equipment or systems than to persuade people to use them. More accidents result from a failure to use equipment properly than from faults in the equipment. The high illegitimate birth rate, for example, is not due to failure of the 'protective equipment' but to the failure of the 'operators', through ignorance, unpreparedness or deliberate choice to use the equipment and methods available.

4. A MANAGER'S GUIDE TO HAZARD ANALYSIS

'Aristotle maintained that women have fewer teeth than men; although he was twice married it never occurred to him to verify this statement by examining his wives' mouths.'
Bertrand Russell

4.1 INTRODUCTION

During the last 100 years managers have become increasingly dependent on the advice of experts of all sorts. The days have long gone when one man — George Stephenson — could survey and construct a railway line, design and construct the engine and drive it on the first run. Perhaps an unconscious desire to be such an engineer is shown by those who display one of Stephenson's engines on their ties!

It is always tempting for a busy man, whether he is managing a plant, workshop or design team, to simply look at the last page of the expert's report and accept his conclusion. The manager cannot, as a rule, check the whole report and even if he had the time it often contains incomprehensible mathematics. This Chapter is intended to help managers locate and check a few key points in reports on hazard analysis.

There should, of course, be a continuing dialogue between the adviser and the advised during the development of the hazard analysis, and in the course of it the manager should ask the questions below. On some occasions a senior manager is presented with an analysis as the justification for a proposal to spend (or not spend) some money, and in these cases he will be questioning a finished or draft report. As a rule the first issues of hazard analysis reports should be drafts.

The following, for ease of style, is addressed to managers. The first point to check is that the three questions in Section 3.3 have been answered.

Does the report:

- Say how often the incident will occur?
- Say how big the consequences will be?
- Recommend what we should do?

4.2 ARITHMETIC, ALGEBRA AND UNITS

As a rule there is no need for the manager to check the arithmetic. To do so is very time consuming, it is unusual to find errors (most that are found do not matter anyway) and the analyst should have had it checked already.

Similarly, there should be no need to check the algebra. If the analyst is experienced he will have combined his rates and probabilities correctly at the 'and' and 'or' gates of his fault trees (see Section 3.5.9). If he is not experienced, he should have had his algebra checked by a more experienced man. If you think that the analyst may be new to the game, ask him who has been over his algebra.

It is, however, useful to look at fault trees or calculations and see that the units are clearly stated at each point, and that rates and probabilities are clearly distinguished. If they are not, they can easily get muddled. Two rates have been multiplied on more than one occasion (see Section 3.5.9).

Also look out for statements in the text, particularly in the conclusion and summaries, such as 'the probability (or target) is 10^{-5}'. Probability of what? — of an incident occurring, or of someone being killed or injured (and, if so, any person or a particular person), per year, per event, per hour or per what?

These, of course, are elementary mistakes made only by inexperienced or amateur analysts.

An amusing example of a failure to quote units is provided by a newspaper article which stated that members of social classes 1 and 2 have a lower probability of dying than the rest of the population. The probability of dying is of course 1 for all of us! The writer meant that the probability of dying per year is lower for a member of social classes 1 and 2.

A reader commented that about half the scientists who have ever lived are still alive, so on the basis of historical evidence, for a scientist the probability of dying is nearer 0.5 than 1! This shows how wrong conclusions can be drawn if we use data unthinkingly without understanding their limitations (see Section 3.6.3).

4.3 THE MODEL

Every hazard analysis is based on a model of the plant and the way hazards arise. As this is often expressed as a fault tree the model is often called 'the logic'.

The analyst rarely knows enough about the plant to draw up the model unaided, and discussion with plant staff is necessary. Nevertheless misunderstandings may arise. If the analyst is an engineer he may not fully understand the chemistry; if a chemist he may not fully understand the engineering. On a new design the drawings, in theory, contain the necessary information on the hardware but do not show how it will be used.

Often a manager explaining a plant to an expert will fail to mention facts which he has come to take for granted but which are not obvious to outsiders. He may thus fail to tell the analyst that one of the chemicals handled freezes at 5°C. The analyst then fails to include frozen pipelines in the list of initiating events which can cause a pipeline to block. Similarly, an analyst may decide to estimate the leak rate from a circulating gas system in the event of pipe failure. The analyst asks for the flow rate and is told that it is, say, 10 000 m^3/h He does not ask and is not told that the total amount of gas in the system is only 1000 m^3.

In checking an analysis, the manager should therefore ask:

- Have any usual properties of the process materials been considered?
- Have any limitations on flow rates, heat inputs, etc, provided by the inventory or equipment been considered?
- Have alternative methods of operation, such as regeneration of catalyst beds, been considered?
- Have start-up and shut-down been considered?
- Does automatic protection protect against all demands or only some of them?
- Has the model been discussed with the maintenance, particularly instrument maintenance, organisation as well as the operating team?

An example of a sophisticated error in the model is provided by the anti-growth movement and their calculations of impending doom.

'In effect, what the Club of Rome report did was to assume that all "bads", such as pollution, demand for food and raw materials, and so on, would increase exponentially for ever and ever, and all "goods", such as techniques to reduce pollution per unit of output, or supplies of food and raw materials, could only increase by finite amounts.

'Clearly, however generous are these finite amounts, it does not need a computer to show that, one day, the "bads" must exceed the "goods".

'... in the words of Lord Ashby[1] — "if we feed doom-laden assumptions into computers it is not surprising that they predict doom".'

The manager should look out for features in a model which make the answers inevitable, regardless of the data.

4.4 THE UNFORESEEN HAZARDS

The biggest errors in hazard analysis arise not in the analysis itself but in the failure to foresee all the causes of hazards or all the hazards that can arise. For example, a study of various methods of transporting a liquefied flammable gas showed that road transport was safer than a pipeline — fewer people would be killed per million tons transported. A manager presented with this result found it hard to believe. By questioning the analyst he discovered that he had taken into account the probability that the tanker driver and others would be killed by a fire or explosion but had ignored the probability that they would be killed by an ordinary road accident (see note at end of Chapter).

A light-hearted example of failure to foresee all the causes of a hazard is provided by a study of 'free meals' (see Section 3.5.9).

In general, ask what methods have been used to identify all the hazards. Has a hazop been done? If not, what other methods have been used to identify hazards?

4.5 THE ASSUMPTIONS

The analysis should include a list of assumptions on which it is based. The manager should look for these and see if he agrees with them. For example, how often are trips, relief valves and other protective devices tested? How often is stand-by equipment tried out? Are the figures quoted realistic and likely to be followed? Is there a monitoring system? Will the testing still be carried out when the start-up manager has left and others have taken his place? These questions are particularly important if the plant is to be located overseas and/or operated by another company which may not have the same attitude towards testing and is not under direct control.

In addition to the listed assumptions, every hazard analysis makes certain assumptions which are usually not written down. The manager should be aware of these and should check their applicability to the particular case. The principal unwritten assumptions are listed in Table 4.1 on page 110.

If assumptions (a) – (d) are not true, then mathematical techniques are available for handling other assumptions, but the need to use them must be recognised (see *Lees*, Chapter 7). Similarly, if we recognise that assumptions (e) and (f) are not true, we can allow for this. If assumption (g) is not true, hazard analysis is a waste of time. As I pointed out in Chapter 1, it is no use calculating the probability of unlikely events if serious incidents are likely as the result of a poor permit-to-work system, lack of instructions, 'Heath Robinson' methods of maintenance and so on. Hazard analysis is a sophisticated technique for good organisations which wish to allocate their resources sensibly and improve their standards. It should not be used until the basic management is satisfactory.

4.6 DATA

Errors can arise because data are inapplicable or misinterpreted (see Sections 3.6.1–3.6.3). The manager should therefore look at the data used to see if they seem about right. For instruments the data are well established and the analyst is unlikely to be far out, but this is not true of mechanical equipment (see Section 6.4).

An example of inapplicable data: The probability of a leak on a flanged pipe joint in a works handling corrosive chemicals was found to be about 10 times higher than on a works handling clean hydrocarbons.

TABLE 4.1

Assumption	Cases in which it may not be true
(a) Failure is random.	During the birth pangs and old age of equipment, and following repairs to machinery. See Section 3.6.7.
(b) Failure rates and demand rates are low.	When failure rates or demand rates are high. (Many of the equations used apply only when failure and demand rates are low.) See Section 3.5.4.
(c) Testing is perfect.	When testing interferes with production.
(d) Repair time is negligible.	When spares are not stocked.
(e) Flows are not limited by inventory.	When flows are high but inventories small. See Section 4.3.
(f) Substances have no unusual properties.	For example, when substances have unusually high (or low) melting or boiling points or are near their critical points. See Section 4.3.
(g) The plant is designed, operated and maintained according to good management and engineering standards.	Overseas, subsidiary or remotely-situated plants which do not receive as much management attention as the main plants ('Rot starts at the edges').

An example of misinterpreted data: A large gearbox required forced lubrication and was provided with two oil pumps, one on-line, one on auto-start. Nevertheless, the calculated rate of failure resulted in the gearbox being starved of oil once in 30 years, a probability that was judged to be too high. Further examination of the data showed that it was based on a published figure for the failure of pumps, but that only 10% of the failures would actually result in immediate loss of oil pressure.

The source of data should be stated even if it is only the 'plant manager's guesstimate'. The example of the Canvey Island Report[2] could usefully be followed and data classified as follows:

- Assessed statistically from historical data: a scientifically-based figure to which a standard deviation could be attached.

- Based on statistics as far as possible but with some missing figures supplied by judgement.
- Estimated by comparison with previous cases for which fault tree assessments have been made.
- 'Dummy' figures — likely to be always uncertain; a subjective judgement must be made.
- Fault tree synthesis: an analytically-based figure which can be independently arrived at by others.

Managers can reasonably expect analysts to classify their data in this or a similar way.

4.7 HUMAN RELIABILITY

Some early hazard analyses ignored the operator, assuming he would always do what he was required to do. Other analysts went to the other extreme, assuming the operator would always fail, and recommended fully-automatic systems.

Nowadays, analysts realise that it is necessary to estimate how often an operator will, for example, close the right valve within the required time when an alarm sounds. However, there is a temptation to overestimate human reliability in order to get the result required. Ask what figures have been used. Some suggestions are given in Section 3.7 and in Reference 4. If the analyst has made significantly different assumptions, his reasons for doing so should be questioned.

As well as errors by operators, errors by people testing and maintaining equipment have to be considered. Has the analyst done so?

The error rates listed in Section 3.7 are about the minimum that can be expected in a well-run organisation due to the inevitable failures of human nature. The remarks made in Section 4.5 about the quality of the management apply here as well. If they do not run a 'tight ship', if people are not trained, if there are no instructions, if no-one cares and monitors, then error rates will be much higher and hazard analysis is a waste of time. First improve the management.

The following is an example of the errors that can easily arise in assessing human reliability: An analysis included an assessment of the probability that a road tanker would be connected up to the wrong pipe. As the two types of tanker in use were fitted with different size connections corresponding to the two sizes of pipe, the chance of a wrong connection seemed small. This view was later revised when it was realised that the operators had collected a vast array of adaptors which enabled them to connect any tanker to any pipe.

4.8 RECOMMENDATIONS

Suppose the analyst has proved to your satisfaction that a hazard is too high and that a proposed course of action will reduce it to an acceptable level at a reasonable cost. The solution has probably been generated by the plant or design team, rather than by the analyst alone, but you should still ask what other solutions have been considered.

Do not confuse a low probability with zero probability. A young doctor was giving patients with Hodgkin's disease (a form of cancer) a treatment which was known to have a cure rate of 90 per cent. He has described his distress when his sixth patient died. He had translated a 90 per cent cure rate into a 100 per cent cure rate and was mentally unprepared for the inevitable failures[5].

In the process industries we often forecast much lower hazard rates; 10^{-5} per year is not uncommon. When a hazard occurs it may be that an unlikely event has occurred by chance (Figure 4.1); it is more likely that one of the assumptions on which the calculation was based is no longer true. For example, testing may have lapsed.

4.9 COMPARISON WITH EXPERIENCE

Is the result of the hazard analysis in accordance with experience and common sense? If not the hazard analysis must be wrong. This is obvious, of course, and

Figure 4.1

would not be worth saying if analysts had not, on a number of occasions, been so carried away by enthusiasm for their calculations that they forgot (like Aristotle) to compare them with experience. For example, a number of theoretical studies of chlorine and ammonia releases have forecast large numbers of casualties. When releases have actually occurred, the casualties have been few. Yet the studies do not say this. It was always realised that casualties could be high if conditions were exactly right and this has been tragically demonstrated by the events at Bhopal. However, most toxic gas releases produce nothing like the theoretically possible number of casualties and the reports should state this.

4.10 CLOSED SHOP OR OPEN SHOP?

Should the managers and the designers call in experts to carry out hazard analyses for them (a closed shop policy) or should managers and designers make their own analyses (an open shop policy)? To quote Kelly *et al*[3]:

'As the level of detail required by the reliability analyst increases, so do his demands on the designer's time and experience. At some point it becomes more effective to train the designer in reliability techniques than to train the reliability analyst in design techniques.'

Hazard analysis is not so esoteric that it can be practised only by an elite band of the initiated. Engineers engaged mainly in design or operations can be trained to apply it. It should be our long-term objective for design teams to carry out their own studies. The experts in hazard analysis should train, check, help and encourage, but not necessarily do all the work.

REFERENCES IN CHAPTER 4

1. Beckerman, W., 23 November 1979, *The Times Higher Education Supplement*, 14.
2. *Canvey —An investigation of potential hazards in the Canvey Island/Thurrock area*, 1978, HMSO, London, 48.
3. Kelly, A.P., Torri, A. and Emon, D.E., 1979, The role of probability analysis in the GCFR safety programme, *NEA/IAEA GCFE Safety Specialist Meeting, Brussels, 13-15 March 1979.*
4. Kletz, T.A., 1991, *An engineer's view of human error*, 2nd edition, Institution of Chemical Engineers, Rugby, UK, especially Chapter 7.
5. Peschel, R. and E., 28 April 1990, *British Medical Journal*, 1145.

While this book was in production the Health and Safety Commission published a detailed quantitative study of the risks of transporting dangerous substances (*Major hazard aspects of the transport of dangerous substances*, HMSO, London, 1991. It compares the risks of road and rail transport, but does not consider ordinary road (or rail) accidents and thus ignores the largest contribution to the road transport risk.

5. OBJECTIONS TO HAZOP AND HAZAN

'She had one major failing in that she tended to quantify benefits. Thus areas of endeavour which could not be quantified, such as education, fell into decline.'
Newspaper report on Mrs Thatcher, November 1990.

This Chapter discusses some of the objections that have been raised to the methods discussed in Chapters 2 and 3, mainly Chapter 3.

5.1 OBJECTIONS TO HAZOP

The main objection to hazop is that it results in expensive additions to plant cost and results in the project being overspent. The main objection to visiting the doctor is that it may result in expensive bills for treatment.

Hazop is a technique for identifying problems. If the remedy is too expensive (and we cannot find a cheaper one) then we can, if we wish, decide to live with the problem. We can say that the remedy is not 'reasonably practicable'. This is a perfectly justifiable stance. (In practice experience shows that there is always, or nearly always, a reasonably practicable way of meeting the targets described in Chapter 3. If the obvious remedy is too expensive, our ability as engineers enables us to find a cheaper solution.) It is not justifiable, however, to fail to look for problems because we may not like what we find.

If you wish to adopt hazop in your company, do not start by setting up a large team. Start by applying it to one or two designs and see if you find it useful. If so, the demand for it will grow (see Section 2.8).

Another objection to hazop is that it takes up the time of the designers and prevents them getting on with the design. Again, this is like not going to see the doctor because we do not have time to do so. If we wait until we become seriously ill we may lose more time in the end. Experience has shown that the time spent in carrying out a hazop, though it may delay completion of the design, is well repaid in a smoother start-up, earlier achievement of flowsheet output and trouble-free operation.

A third objection is discussed in Section 2.4.4.

One company has suggested that to save time a hazop should look only for departures from their design standards[5]. This may be acceptable if the process is a familiar one in which all hazards have been recognised and allowed for but if we are innovating, and there is usually some innovation, new hazards may not be recognised. Also, in most companies, standards lag behind the latest information and ideas.

5.2 TECHNICAL OBJECTIONS TO HAZAN

5.2.1 INSUFFICIENT DATA ARE AVAILABLE FOR MEANINGFUL CALCULATIONS

It is true that the application of the technique is often limited by the availability of data. Good data are available on instruments and on standard fittings such as relief valves, and such data from one company or organisation can be applied in another, with little error. But the same is not true of most mechanical equipment, as discussed in Sections 3.6.1–3.6.3 and 6.4. Failure rates depend on the environment, on the maintenance policy and on the way the equipment is treated. In-house data usually has to be used.

However, even if little data are available, meaningful calculations may be possible, as illustrated by the following. Should a remotely-operated emergency isolation valve be installed in the suction line of a pump to isolate any major leaks that occur? Manual isolation will be impossible as most leaks will catch fire. The fire damage, including loss of production, is estimated at about £100 000 but we do not know how often the pump will leak.

The cost of installing the remotely operated valve is £10 000 or, say, £3000/year (depreciation, maintenance and return on capital). If the probability of a major leak is greater than once in 33 years the expenditure is justified. We may not need to start looking for failure data on pumps. Our experience may tell us that particularly on a hot or cold duty the failure rates of our pumps are well above this figure.

5.2.2 THE MODELS OF THE ACCIDENTS ARE SO OVERSIMPLIFIED THAT THEY BEAR LITTLE RELATION TO REALITY

This is sometimes true but many accident scenarios are simple and the examples discussed in References 11–13 of Chapter 3 show how quite complex situations can be modelled. Much more complex situations have been modelled on nuclear reactors and on an ethylene oxide plant[1].

5.2.3 NOT ALL HAZARDS WILL HAVE BEEN IDENTIFIED SO IT IS POINTLESS QUANTIFYING THOSE THAT HAVE BEEN

This can be a valid objection. Chapters 2 and 3 have stressed the importance of identifying hazards. It is little use quantifying some hazards if larger ones have been overlooked.

5.2.4 HUMAN ERRORS, INCLUDING MANAGEMENT ERRORS, CANNOT BE ALLOWED FOR

Section 3.7 shows that it is possible to take human error into account and the examples discussed in detail in References 11–13 and 25 of Chapter 3 show how this is done.

Several systems have now been devised for carrying out an audit of the management, awarding marks under various headings and multiplying equipment failure rates, or the overall risk for a site, by factors which may vary over a wide range[20–22].

However, as already stated in Chapter 1 and Section 4.5, if management is incompetent, it is better to improve the management than introduce sophisticated techniques.

5.2.5 THE RESOURCES REQUIRED ARE EXCESSIVE

As with hazop, do not start with a large team. Start by applying hazan to one or two problems and see if people find it useful. If so, the demand for the technique will grow.

All service functions can grow out-of-hand if they are allowed to tackle every problem that the clients bring forward. As discussed in Chapter 1, hazan should be applied only to those problems that cannot be answered by reference to experience or generally accepted up-to-date codes of practice.

If there are more problems to be analysed than can be dealt with in the time available, then a rapid ranking technique can be used to put the problems into a sort of batting order so that the biggest risks, or those about which least is known, can be studied first. For example, the hazards can be assigned to one of the five categories shown in Table 5.1 and the expected frequency of occurrence compared with the bottom line of Table 5.1. Table 5.2 (see page 118) is then used to derive priorities between A, the highest, and D, the lowest[6]. Note that this is not a technique for rapid hazard analysis but merely a technique for helping us decide which hazards should be analysed first.

A somewhat similar technique has been devised for the rapid assessment of less serious hazards when the size of the risk makes a full hazard analysis unnecessary (and, very often, the sparcity of data makes it impossible)[7].

5.2.6 IT CANNOT BE APPLIED TO INDUSTRIAL DISEASE

Reference 3 describes an attempt to compare hazards which produce immediate effects with those which produce long-term effects. The results indicate that the allocation of resources between the two sorts of hazards is not out by more than an order of magnitude. This may not sound very good but is not bad for problems of resource allocation. As shown in Section 3.4.7 the implicit values given to saving a life can vary over a range of a million to one.

As an example consider ionising radiation. If we have more resources available for saving life, should we spend them on preventing accidents which kill people quickly, or on reducing exposure to radiation?

TABLE 5.1
Principles of hazard categorisation for rapid ranking (from Reference 6)

Area at risk	Description of risk	Hazard category 1	2	3	4	5
Plant	Damage	Minor < £2000	Appreciable < £20 000	Major < £200 000	Severe < £2M	Total destruction > £2M
	Effect on personnel	Minor injuries only	Injuries	1 in 10 chance of a fatality	Fatality	Multiple fatalities
Works	Damage	None	None	Minor	Appreciable	Severe
Business	Business loss	None	None	Minor	Severe	Total loss of business
Public	Damage	None	Very minor	Minor	Appreciable	Severe
	Effects on people	None (smells)	Minor	Some hospitalisation	1 in 10 chance of public fatality	Fatality
	Reaction	None/mild	Minor local outcry	Considerable local and national press reaction	Severe local and considerable national press reaction	Severe national (pressure to stop business)
Relative guide frequency of occurrence		1	10^{-1}	10^{-2}	10^{-3}	10^{-4}
Typical* judgmental values for a plant/small works		1/yr	1/10 yrs	1/100 yrs	1/1000 yrs	$1/10^4$ yrs

* N.B. These typical comparative figures are given for illustration and should not be taken as applicable to all situations nor taken to indicate absolute levels of acceptability.

The International Committee on Radiological Protection recommend that the maximum dose for an employee should not exceed 50 millisieverts (mSv) /year. For many years it was believed that this would give a risk of death of 5×10^{-5} per year or a FAR (see Section 3.4.1) of 25. Very few people are actually exposed to the maximum dose but nevertheless it does seem rather high when we bear in mind that the average FAR for manufacturing industry in the

TABLE 5.2
Rapid ranking: final ranking (from Reference 6)

Hazard category (see Table 5.1)	Expected frequency compared with guide frequency			
	Smaller (–)	**Same (=)**	**Greater (+)**	**Uncertain (U)**
1	D	D	D/C at team's discretion	
2	D	Normally C, but if upper end of frequency/ potential raised to B at team's discretion.	Equally damaging hazard as those below A but if lower end of frequency/ potential could be lowered to B at team's discretion.	B Frequency estimates should not be difficult at this category; may be a lack of fundamental knowledge which requires research.
3	C	B	A Major hazard	A/B at team's discretion. Such potential should be better understood.
4 and 5	B/C at team's discretion.	B, but can be raised to A at team's discretion.	A Major hazard	A Such potential should be better understood.

UK is 2. Much of the UK chemical industry regards 2 as an upper level for all chemical risks (Section 3.4.1) and people exposed to ionising radiation are also exposed to other risks as well.

However, the radioactivity dose limits 'are not to be taken as a target, but rather as the lower limit of values that are not acceptable ... a properly managed practice should never expose workers or the public to anywhere near the limit'[25].

There is now evidence that the risk from radiation may be as much as three times higher than was originally thought, but to compensate for this the nuclear industry in the UK has set 15 mSv/y as the level which should not be exceeded.

Similar comparisons are made in Reference 3 for coal dust, asbestos, chemicals as a whole and industry as a whole.

In considering these comparisons, remember that acute risks such as fires, explosions, falls and some toxic chemicals kill people immediately while radiation (and many toxic chemicals) kill them 20–40 years later. Many people argue that a higher death rate from these long-term risks is therefore tolerable. On the other hand industrial disease may produce many years of illness and reduced quality of life followed by death at the time of retirement when one is looking forward to well-earned leisure. Perhaps these effects can be offset and all deaths regarded as equally undesirable. Whatever our views it seems that the risks from acute and long-term risks are within a factor of ten and that the allocation of resources between them in the past has not been too far out.

5.2.7 IT IS OFTEN DONE BADLY

Perhaps, but if so we should learn to do it better. If some people say that 2 + 3 = 6, we do not say that arithmetic is useless and should not be used. Instead we suggest that they learn to do it properly.

Writing in 1980 about the nuclear industry, Joksimovic and Vesely[23] commented:

'It's amazing how many risk "experts" instantly surface when agencies and companies are willing to spend money on risk analyses. In every useful PRA to be performed in the near future, we would hazard a guess that there might be at least 10 useless "number crunching" exercises performed. The trick might be to see the rose in the weed patch.

'In spite of these problems and pitfalls, we continue to be optimistic because of our convictions that PRA provides the only way to address and balance many nuclear safety issues.'

5.2.8 THE RESULTS DO NOT AGREE WITH THOSE OBTAINED BY OTHER METHODS OF CALCULATION

During the Sizewell B public inquiry widely different figures were produced for the failure rates of large pressure vessels. Extrapolations from experience produced higher figures than metallurgical studies. To understand the reasons for the difference consider the probability that the sun will fail to rise tomorrow morning[8]. My experience covers about 25 000 days and during that time the sun has risen every morning. I am therefore 86 per cent confident, on the basis of experience, that the chance that the sun will not rise tomorrow morning is less than 1 in 12 500[9]. It may be very much less but experience is no guide. However, I have other reasons for believing that the probability is a lot less than the figure quoted. A model has been developed to explain the movements of the heavenly bodies and it fits observations so well that we have a high degree of confidence in its accuracy.

5.2.9 NO-ONE WILL TAKE ANY ACCOUNT OF THE RESULTS OF THE HAZARD ANALYSIS IN MAKING DECISIONS

This may be true if we are considering risks which have become the subject of public debate. Governments, local authorities, the media, pressure groups and the public may continue to press for what they want. However, the vast majority of hazard analyses are concerned with in-plant problems in which emotions are not aroused. Even when emotions are aroused, we should put forward the facts and hope that in time reason will prevail (but see Section 5.3).

5.2.10 YOU CANNOT DECIDE EVERYTHING ON NUMBERS

Of course you cannot. Hazard analysis is an aid to management judgement, not a machine for making decisions. But managers will make better judgements if they have relevant information, especially numerical information.

If your gut feeling (or experienced judgement, to give it a more high-sounding title) differs from the results of an analysis, you should try to puzzle out and explain the reasons for the difference. Is it past experience of a similar situation, suspicion of technical arguments you cannot fully understand, distrust of someone's judgement? If you can put your feelings into words you are more likely to convince others.

What are the alternative methods you can use if you decide to ignore a hazard analysis? The first is to rely entirely on 'gut feeling'. Unfortunately different guts feel differently and a dialogue is difficult. Numerical methods do allow a dialogue to take place. If one person says that risk A is high and another that it is not, a dialogue is difficult. If we have a scale for measuring risks a dialogue becomes possible (see Section 2.9).

In making a decision in matters that affect the public a manager must take public opinion into account. Ultimately, in a democracy, governments must act in accordance with public opinion. They may have to take action that their own judgement tells them is incorrect. This is part of the democratic process. The advocates of hazard analysis do not seek an alternative to public opinion;

they seek to persuade it. Hazard analysis may also provide an antidote to a policy of giving the most to those who shout the loudest.

Public opinion should not, of course, be confused with the opinion of the media or of self-appointed pressure groups.

A more philosophical objection to hazard analysis is that deaths from industrial accidents, smoking, sport and contaminants in food are not the same and therefore cannot be compared. However, comparing different things is what management is about. Resources are not unlimited and we have to decide how to allocate them between safety, protection of the environment, improving working conditions, increasing the wealth of the community and so on. Information on the relative sizes of various risks and the costs of removing them will help us to make better decisions. Of course, we also have to take into account the public's aversion to different risks, as discussed in the next Section. And while deaths from different causes are undoubtably different they are probably less different than most of the alternatives we have to choose between, at work and in everyday life. We are just as dead whichever way we die.

Some writers, notably Cotgrove[4], have suggested that much of the opposition to hazard analysis comes from people who have a different paradigm or set of values to those who advocate technological advance. They are more concerned with protection of the environment, for example, than with output or efficiency. They oppose the values of technologists rather than the systematic allocation of resources but the two are linked in their minds. In fact, though it shows that some risks are trivial and hardly worth bothering about, hazard analysis has probably resulted in a large increase in expenditure on safety.

Accountants try to quantify everything financial and thus, according to Malpas and Watson[26], overlook what they call 'Options for the future', that is, expenditure which does not show a good rate of return but nevertheless makes it possible to pursue promising lines of development.

5.3 POPULAR OBJECTIONS TO HAZAN

A number of writers have analysed the factors that determine the public's attitude to risks and the following is based on the work of Lee[10], Slovic *et al*[11], Sandman[12] and Kauffman[18].

The probability of an incident is, of course, one of the factors that the public take into account but not the only one, and even here the public's knowledge of the relative size of different probabilities is often far removed from their actual sizes. Their knowledge of the numbers killed by different hazards is not too far out but their knowledge of relative rates bears little relation to reality. For example, the risk from pesticide residues in food, a subject of popular

Figure 5.1

concern, is far less than the risk from natural poisons. Other factors that affect the public's attitude are:

VOLUNTARY OR IMPOSED?

We accept without complaint risks such as smoking or rock-climbing that we choose to follow but object to risks such as those from industry that are imposed on us without our permission. For this reason many writers believe it may be counterproductive to use cigarettes as a unit of risk (Figure 5.1).

UNDER OUR CONTROL

We accept more readily risks, such as driving, that we feel are under our control, than risks such as those from industry, railway accidents or pollution that are not under our control. We hold the meat closer to the knife if we are holding the knife.

NATURAL OR MAN-MADE

We accept more readily natural risks such as those from floods, storms, radon and natural foods and drugs than man-made risks such as those from industry, nuclear power stations, pesticides, food additives and synthetic drugs. This is one of the less defensible of the public's views. In part, it is due to the mistaken belief that little can be done about Acts of God, as they are sometimes called; in fact, floods, droughts and famines are due to mismanagement rather than too much or too little rain while the effects of earthquakes, volcanos and hurricanes are often magnified by mismanagement[13]. In part, the public's attitude is due to an equally mistaken belief that natural foods and drugs are always good for us. In fact, the average US diet contains about 1.5 g/day of natural pesticides but only about 0.15 mg/day of synthetic pesticides. Many of the natural pesticides present in food would never be approved if they were tested in the same way as synthetic pesticides[14,15]. Similarly, natural drugs can be sold without going through the rigorous testing necessary for new synthetic drugs. Plants contain natural pesticides because they cannot pull up their roots and run away or fight back with tooth and claw; their only defense is to poison their enemies.

FAMILIARITY

We readily accept familiar risks such as those of driving, long-established drugs such as aspirin and traditional industries such as farming, but are less ready to accept unfamiliar risks such as those of new drugs and nuclear power. We know the size of familiar hazards (Figure 5.2). Road accidents kill about 5000 people

Figure 5.2

per year in the UK. This is terrible but at least the extent is known; we are confident that the number killed this year will not be 10 000. In contrast, although we may agree that nuclear power and the chemical industry will probably kill no-one this year, we cannot be sure there will not be another Bhopal or another Chernobyl.

EXPERIENCE

If we have had personal experience of a risk, we are wary of it in future. If shellfish, say, have made us ill we may avoid them in the future even though we know that we are unlikely to be offered another contaminated batch. Similarly, if the local factory has caused pollution in the past we tend not to believe assurances that all will be well in the future.

DREAD

Heart disease kills about twice as many people as cancer but nevertheless many people would support the expenditure of greater sums on cancer prevention as cancer inspires so much more dread. This is not a decision made in ignorance as almost every family has experience of both.

I BENEFIT

We accept risks from which we earn a living or derive other benefits. We accept the risk of driving because the benefits of the car are clear and obvious. The benefits of the chemical industry are not obvious. All it seems to do is to produce unpleasant chemicals with unpronounceable names in order to increase its sordid profits. At best, it provides employment and exports. Most people do not realise that it provides the essentials for a standard of living that has vastly improved the length and quality of life.

MORALITY

Far more people are killed by cars than are murdered, but murder is still less acceptable. We would be outraged if the police stopped trying to catch murderers, or child abusers, and looked for dangerous drivers instead, even if more lives would be saved in that way.

NUMBERS MORE IMPORTANT THAN RATE

The airlines realised twenty or more years ago that as the number of flights increased the number of accidents could not be allowed to increase in proportion or there would be a public outcry. They found it possible to decrease the rate so that the number remained roughly constant. Similarly, we find the death of ten people at a time less acceptable than the death of one person per year for ten years (see Section 3.4.3).

ASSOCIATIONS

Nuclear power reminds us of atomic bombs; electricity from the sun, wind or water reminds us of pleasant summer days in the fresh air. The reality is rather different; more people have been killed by the collapse of dams than by any other peacetime artifact (see the note at the end of this Chapter.)

PUBLICITY

The more space the press devote to a hazard, the greater it is perceived to be. Drugs that could relieve the pain and suffering of many are withdrawn when the press highlight adverse effects in a few users.

THE VICTIMS ARE KNOWN IN ADVANCE

There is almost no limit to the resources we will spend to rescue someone trapped in an old mine, for example, but we do little to help those who will be killed on the roads next week as we do not know who they will be.

JUDGING THE MESSENGER

If we can't understand the message, we judge the messenger. The spokesman for industry, a new drug, pesticides or any other hazard, real or perceived, is more likely to be listened to if he comes across as an open, courteous, caring person who admits past mistakes, speaks in language we can understand and is one of us. The last may be the most difficult as the industry or company spokesman is often more educated than his audience, has a different accent and comes from a different part of the country. An anthropologist, describing his attempts to relate to a group of fisherman, wrote[16], ' ... they said that my speech, like my clothes, was too clean ... the Ranger also told me ... , "Your body language just didn't fit in with theirs ... you stood too erect, while they tend to slouch with their thumbs cocked in their pockets. And you made too much eye contact, while they prefer to look away and fidget"'.

Sandman admits that real people die because we are more concerned about the factors discussed here than about the actual probability of being killed. But, he adds, we also value fairness, moral values and individual freedom, sometimes more than life itself.

It is not sufficient therefore to present the facts and hope that in time the public will accept them; the power of a belief does not depend on its truth. We should also try to answer the public's concerns, rational and irrational. Unfortunately most of these concerns tend to make the man in the street oppose the chemical and nuclear industries (the risks are imposed, not under his control, man-made, unfamiliar and dreaded; past experience has been unpleasant; the industries do not obviously benefit him; and the spokesmen for the industries are often outsiders) and this is reinforced by the media's desire for disaster, their daily bread (every reporter has Jeremiah as a middle name). There is no easy solution but the improvement in the image of British Nuclear Fuels during the late 1980s shows what can be done.

Ultimately, if the experts cannot convince the public that a risk is negligible, they will have to remove or reduce it. This, after all, is democracy in action. In 1983 Fremlin[24] wrote, 'When little children are afraid of the dark, you put a light there, even though you know there is nothing to be afraid of. It would therefore be sensible if the Government insisted now on getting the amounts [of radioactive material] dispersed from Windscale reduced, not because this if faintly necessary to reduce cancer, but in order to show people that they care, and to put their minds at rest'. Since then the Government have followed his advice.

FURTHER READING

See Reference 2 and References 18–22 of Chapter 3. Reference 27 is a good introduction to the risks of energy production.

A NOTE ON DAMS (see Section 5.3, item 10)

In August 1979 a dam collapsed in India. I quoted (in Reference 17) a press report which said that 15 000 people had been killed. After someone had cast doubt on this figure a search through back numbers of The Daily Telegraph for August and September 1979[19] found the following reports on the numbers killed:

13 August:	A thousand to several thousand
14 August:	Up to 3000
15 August:	Up to 25 000
18 August:	Hundreds
23 August:	At least 1405; earlier the Mayor had said at least 25 000.
11 September:	More than 2000.

The incident may therefore have killed more people than Bhopal. Whatever the true figure, no-one seems to have cared very much or commented on the discrepancies. Why are people so much more concerned about chemical engineering disasters than civil engineering disasters? Perhaps because dams have pleasant associations, reminding us of summer days in the country, but chemical factories do not.

REFERENCES IN CHAPTER 5

1. Stewart, R.M., 1971, High integrity protective systems, *Symposium Series No. 34*, Institution of Chemical Engineers, Rugby, UK, 99.
2. Joschek, H.I., January 1983, *Plant/Operations Progress*, 2 (1): 1.

3. Kletz, T.A., 1988, in *Engineering risk and hazard assessment*, Volume 1, edited by A. Kandel and E. Avni, CRC Press, Boca Raton, Florida, 1.
4. Cotgrove, S., 1981, Risk, value judgement and political legitimacy, in *Dealing with risk*, edited by R.F. Griffiths, Manchester University Press, Manchester, UK, 122.
5. Solomon, C.H., August 1983, *Loss Prevention Bulletin*, No. 052, 10.
6. Gillett, J., February 1985, *Process Engineering*, 66 (2): 19.
7. Keey, R.B., May 1991, *Process Safety and Environmental Protection*, 69 (B2): 85.
8. *Sizewell B Public Inquiry: Transcript of Proceedings*, 8 June 1984.
9. Kletz, T.A., 1990, *Improving chemical industry practices —a new look at old myths of the chemical industry*, Hemisphere, New York, 92.
10. Lee, T.R., 1986, *The Science of the Total Environment*, 51: 125.
11. Slovic, P.B., Fischhoff, B. and Lichtenstein, S., 1980, Facts and fears: understanding perceived risks, in *Societal risk assessment*, edited by R. C. Schwing and W. A. Albers, Plenum Press, New York, 181.
12. Sandman, P.M., 1989, Hazard versus outrage: how the public sees environmental risk, *American Institute of Chemical Engineers Summer Meeting, Philadelphia, Pennsylvania, 21 August 1989*
13. Wijkman, A. and Timberlake, L., 1986, *Natural disasters —acts of God or acts of man?*, International Institute for Research and Development, London, 1986, 6, 29 and 30.
14. Johnson, J., February 1991, *Chemistry in Britain*, 27 (2): 112.
15. Ames, B.N., October 1989, *Chemtech*, 590.
16. Gmelch, G., September 1990, *Natural History*, 32.
17. *Health and Safety at Work*, August 1986, 8: 10.
18. Kauffman, G.B., 1991, *Chemistry in Britain*, 27 (6): 512
19. Chaney, M., private communication.
20. Pitblado, R.M., Williams, J.C. and Slater, D.H., July 1991, *Plant/Operations Progress*, 9 (3): 169.
21. Hurst, N.W., Bellamy, L.J., Geyer, T.A.W. and Astley, J.A., 1991, *Journal of Hazardous Materials*, 26: 159.
22. Hurst, N.W., 1991, Immediate and underlying causes of vessel failures: Implications for including management and organisational factors in quantified risk assessment, *Symposium Series No. 124*, Institution of Chemical Engineers, Rugby, UK, 155.
23. Jokosimovic, V. and Vesely, W.E., July/September 1980, *Reliability Engineering*, 1 (1): 72.
24. Fremlin, J.H., 21 November 1983, quoted in *The Daily Telegraph*.
25. Kovan, R. and Conway, A., September 1991, *Atom*, No. 416, 20.
26. Malpas, R. and Watson, S.J.J., 1991, *Technology and wealth creation*, Fellowship of Engineering, London.
27. Luton Industrial College, 1991, *Energy – a matter of life and death*, Merlin Books, Braunton, Devon.

APPENDIX TO CHAPTER 5

The following letter appeared in *Reliability Engineering*, 1981, 2: 77. It shows how arguments with some merit may be used to arrive at the wrong conclusion.

LIMITATIONS ON THE APPLICATION OF QUANTITATIVE METHODS TO RAILWAY TRAVEL

At first sight a railway timetable appears to offer a precise, numerical and generally applicable method for calculating the time required for a railway journey and the probable starting and finishing times. However, experience over a number of years has shown that this optimism is not justified and the limitations of the method are such as to render it unsuitable for widespread application, though it may be useful in a few limited areas.

The serious limitations on the use of railway timetables result from the following well-established facts:

- The answers obtained assume that all possible routes between the starting and finishing points are known and have therefore been investigated. In fact, this is often not the case and routes which have not been thought of provide possible pathways, particularly under abnormal operating conditions such as Sundays, Bank Holidays and nights.
- The timetable is an expression of intention or, at the best, of past performance, rather than of future performance. It is not unknown for trains to fail to run or to run late.
- The railways are subject to human error on the part of the drivers, signalmen and station staff. Numerous detailed reports, over many years, have established this beyond reasonable doubt. There is no satisfactory way of making allowance for these errors in estimating journey times, despite the considerable effort expended in recent years on the study of human reliability.
- The complexity of the timetables is such that extensive, detailed and time-consuming studies are necessary to evaluate journey times. The necessary resources of manpower and time are rarely available.
- Timetable data are usually shown to a degree of accuracy that is untrue and misleading. Times of arrival and departure are shown to the nearest minute for journeys that may take ten hours or more. Users are misled into thinking that a degree of accuracy is attainable that is not, in fact, the case.

It is clear that the use of railway timetables for the estimation of journey durations and arrival and departure times cannot be recommended and that they should not be used for this purpose — just turn up at the station and hope there will be a train.

6. SOURCES OF DATA AND CONFIDENCE LIMITS

'Errors using inadequate data are much less than those using no data at all.'
Charles Babbage (1792–1871)

6.1 DATA BANKS AND DATA BOOKS

Errors caused by using inapplicable data were discussed in Sections 3.6.1–3.6.3. This Section provides a few notes on sources of data.

The best source of data, especially for instruments and electrical equipment, is the Data Bank operated by the Systems Reliability Service of the UK Atomic Energy Authority (AEA), at Warrington, UK. Member organisations pay an annual subscription and are expected to contribute data. In return they have access to the data provided by the AEA and by other subscribers. The American Institute of Chemical Engineers have also published a book of data[4] and Dhillon and Viswanath[5] have listed 367 sources of data.

Many large companies have produced their own data books which summarise data obtained from the AEA, the literature and internal sources. Unfortunately these are often misused. The intention of the compilers is that a reader will look in the data book to see if there are any data on, say, relief valve failure rates and will then consult the original references for details. Unfortunately many users take a figure from the data book, do not bother to consult the original source and may miss important qualifications.

For example, there is a well-known report on pressure vessel failures[1] which gives a 'catastrophic failure rate' of 4.2×10^{-5} per vessel-year. It defines 'catastrophic failure' as 'destruction of the vessel or component, or a failure so severe as to necessitate major repairs or replacement'. The definition thus includes defects which are found during inspection and do not result in a leak. The figure is often quoted without the definition. Readers who do not take the trouble to refer to the original paper assume that 'catastrophic' means destruction in service with release of the contents, and are misled.

Data are discussed by *Lees*, Chapter 7, Section 15, while his Appendix 9 lists much published data and gives references to other sources. References 6 and 7 also provide some data and Reference 6 has a chapter on data banks.

According to Young[8], Exxon has collected data on the probability of losses of various sizes on various types of refinery and chemical plant equipment. Their graphs of loss against probability are the financial equivalent of the *F–N* curves described in Section 3.4.4. He quotes a few examples. For one type of equipment — he does not say which — the probability of a loss of $10M or greater (1986 prices) is 4 in 10 000 years and the probability of a loss of $1000 is 1 in 100 years. Such data, if they became generally available, could be used to carry out hazard analyses of the type described at the beginning of Section 3.4 in which we compare the cost of an incident with the cost of prevention.

6.2 IF FAILURE HAS NEVER OCCURRED

If failure of a component has never occurred in, say, 100 component-years of operation, it is often assumed that a failure will occur in the next year. We can then be 86% confident that the average failure rate is one in 50 component-years or less. It may be very much less (see Section 5.2.8 and Reference 2).

If there are many components in a system and many of them have never failed, it is straining credulity to assume that they will all fail next year.

Sometimes no failure data are available and an estimate has to be supplied by an experienced person. Some people may then ask, 'If we have to estimate the failure data, why not estimate the answer to the whole problem?'.

If we break problems down into their component parts, answering them with facts when possible and with opinion only when no facts are available, we are more likely to get a correct answer than if we try to guess the answer to the whole problem.

Fault tree calculations are not 'series' calculations in which a 10% error in the input is carried through to the output. They are 'parallel' calculations in which different streams are combined and most errors in the data have little effect on the final answer.

If we put 10% impurity in the water entering a long pipeline without branches, there will be 10% impurity in the output, However, if we put 10% impurity in one of the streams feeding a river, there will not be 10% impurity in the water reaching the sea.

6.3 CONFIDENCE LIMITS

Hazard analysis is not an exact science. Many estimates of the probability of an incident can be out by a factor of 3 or 4, and a factor of 10 is by no means uncommon. Estimates are usually conservative as analysts prefer to err on the safe side. Relatively few estimates have been validated by experience; inevitably so, as most deal with rare events. One study[3] looked at the estimated reliabilities of 130 different engineering systems and pieces of equipment and showed that 10% of the observed values were within a factor of two of the estimate, 90% within a factor of four.

Different estimates of consequences may differ greatly, particularly where gas dispersion is involved, but in recent years the estimates have converged.

Hazard analysts could well place estimates on the accuracy of their data (see Section 4.6) and the final result. But the meaning of such confidence limits should be made clear. They can allow for uncertainties in the data but not for errors in the logic, for failure to identify all the ways in which hazards can occur or for errors in estimates of human reliability. In practice the first two are usually much more important than errors in the data.

Even the uncertainties in the data allowed for in the confidence limits are not the complete range of uncertainties. The confidence limits allow for uncertainties due to sample size but not, of course, to errors due to changes in design, use of inapplicable data and so on.

Suppose a hazard analysis shows that an event will occur on average once in 100 years. If the event occurs next year (or next week) this does not prove that the estimate was wrong (though it may be). If the event occurs randomly, then it is equally likely to occur in any year in the next 100 years. This point is misunderstood by many people.

On the other hand, few accidents occur because the unlikely odds of one in so many thousand years actually come off (see Section 4.8). More often, after an accident has occurred, it is found that some of the assumptions on which the analysis was based are incorrect. For example, testing of protective equipment has lapsed or is not thorough, or the faults found are not promptly rectified.

6.4 DATA ON MECHANICAL EQUIPMENT MAY BE DATA ON PEOPLE

The failure rate of instruments is much the same, within a factor of about four, for all industries and environments (*Lees*, Section 13.6). We can use someone else's data with confidence. With mechanical equipment the situation is different. As the examples of bellows and vending machines in Section 3.6.3 show, the failure rate can vary a good deal between one plant and another depending on the conditions of use and the quality of installation and maintenance. Data on pipework failures tell us more about the quality of design and construction than about the inherent properties of the pipe. Machinery sometimes fails because it has not been lubricated correctly; failure data then tell us something about the training and competence of the operating team but little about the inherent properties of the machinery. It tells us that the machinery will not withstand lack of lubrication but we probably know that already[9].

Of course, whenever possible we should use user-friendly plants which cannot be assembled incorrectly and which can withstand poor maintenance and operation[10] (see Section 5.2.4).

REFERENCES IN CHAPTER 6

1. Smith, T.A. and Warwick, R.G., 1981, *A survey of pressure vessels in the UK for the period 1962–1978 and its relevance to nuclear primary circuits, Report No. SRD R 203*, UK Atomic Energy Authority, Warrington, UK.
2. Kletz, T.A., 1990, *Improving chemical industry practices —a new look at old myths of the chemical industry*, Hemisphere, New York, 92.
3. Smith, E.R., August 1981, *The correlation between the predicted and the observed reliabilities of components, equipment and systems, Report No. NCSR R18*, UK Atomic Energy Authority, Warrington, UK.
4. *Guidelines for process equipment reliability data*, 1990, American Institute of Chemical Engineers, New York.
5. Dhillon, B.S. and Viswanath, H.C., 1990, *Microelectronic Reliability*, 30 (4): 723.
6. Green, A.E. and Bourne, J.R., 1972, *Reliability technology*, Wiley, Chichester, UK.
7. Green, A.E. (editor), 1982, *High risk safety technology*, Wiley, Chichester, UK.
8. Young, R.S, 1986, Risk analysis applied to refinery safety expenditure, *American Petroleum Institute Committee on Safety and Fire Protection Spring Meeting, 8 – 11 April 1986.*
9. Kletz, T.A., 1985, *Reliability Engineering*, 11 (4): 185.
10. Kletz, T.A., 1991, *Plant design for safety —a user-friendly approach*, Hemisphere, New York.

7. THE HISTORY OF HAZOP AND HAZAN

'No revolutionary idea arises without a pedigree.'
S. J. Gould[6]

' ... while (Leonardo da Vinci's) mechanics and engineering are, for their breadth and depth of experience, unique and at times ahead of their times, they are not a fruit ripened alone in a desert.'
M. Cianchi[7]

7.1 HAZOP

In 1963 the Heavy Organic Chemicals (HOC, later Petrochemicals) Division of ICI was designing a plant for the production of phenol and acetone from cumene. It was a time when the cry was for 'minimum capital cost' (rather than minimum lifetime cost or maximum profit) and the design had been pruned of all inessential features. Some people felt that it had been pruned too far. It was also a time when method study and, in particular, 'critical examination' were in vogue. Critical examination is a formal technique for examining an activity and generating alternatives by asking, 'What is achieved?', 'What else could be achieved?' and so on, as shown in Table 7.1.

The production manager, K.W. Gee, had recently spent a year in ICI's Central Work Study Department. (The status of work study was so high at the time that a high flier could be seconded there for a year.) He decided to see if critical examination could be applied to the design of the phenol plant in order to bring out into the open any deficiencies in design and find the best way of spending any extra money that might be available. A team was set up including the commissioning manager (J. A. Wade), the plant manager (A. Barker) and an expert in method study and critical examination (G. B. Harron). During 1964 they met for three full days per week for four months, examining the phenol plant line diagrams and covering acres of paper with all the questions and answers. They discovered many potential hazards and operating problems that had not been forseen, modifying the technique as they did so. Harron later wrote, 'We concocted an approach for trial ... and to cut a long story short this approach did not work. Not because it did not do the job but because it was too detailed, penetrated into too many corners, all good stuff but life was just too short. After a good many tries we came up with an approach which has much of the principle of critical examination but was somewhat bent in style'. The essence of the new approach was that a technique designed to identify alternatives was modified so that it identified deviations[8]. It was recognisably hazop as we know it today though it was further modified during later studies to the form described in Chapter 2.

TABLE 7.1
Critical examination

METHOD STUDY: CRITICAL EXAMINATION SHEET			
Description of element . . . . Reference . . . . Page . . . . Date			
The present facts		**Alternatives**	**Selection for development**
WHAT is achieved?	WHY?	What ELSE could be achieved?	What SHOULD be achieved?
HOW is it achieved?	WHY THAT WAY?	How ELSE could it be achieved?	How SHOULD it be achieved?
WHEN is it achieved?	WHY THEN?	When ELSE could it be achieved?	When SHOULD it be achieved?
WHERE is it achieved?	WHY THERE?	Where ELSE could it be achieved?	Where SHOULD it be achieved?
WHO achieved it?	WHY THAT PERSON?	Who ELSE could achieve it?	Who SHOULD achieve it?

The following are a few of the safety points that came out of this early hazop (though that term was not used then; the exercise was described as a method study or hazard investigation). Some of the points are now included in design specifications but were not included at the time.

- By-passes around control valves which are connected to safety trips should be deleted. Use of a by-pass renders the safety trip useless.
- Nitrogen should be used for vacuum breaking to prevent the ingress of air into a hot system.
- Break tanks should be fitted in the town water supply to prevent contamination by reverse flow.
- The relief valve system should be checked for places in which liquid could collect.
- A slip-plate should be fitted in the feed line to [vessel X] to prevent liquid leaking in before conditions are correct.
- Vent valves should be fitted to all blowing points so that the pressure can be blown off before hoses are disconnected.
- A vent valve should be fitted to a high pressure filter so that the pressure can be blown off before the filter is opened for cleaning.
- Extended spindles should be fitted to the valves on acid tanks to reduce the risk that operators may be splashed by leaks.
- Special equipment should be designed for charging and discharging catalysts and other auxiliary materials, to remove the dangers that go with improvisation.

Note that all these points are written as recommendations. Today most hazop teams would not say 'should' but simply 'Delete by-passes ... etc'.

More operating points than safety ones came out of the study. This was expected. The remit of the team was 'To devote themselves full-time to obtaining and studying information from all sources and to take any necessary decisions on broad plant design aimed at ensuring that the phenol plant would start up quickly and satisfactorily; that it will produce its design output and quality of products; that it will operate safely and its effluents will be satisfactorily treated'. Today many, perhaps most, hazops produce more operating points than safety ones.

A few months before the phenol study was undertaken in ICI HOC Division at Billingham the Mond Division at Runcorn carried out a similar but very much shorter study (it occupied a team of four for 21 hours) on a semi-technical plant. The remit for this study was 'To evaluate the process for hazards which may arise during operation of the semi-technical plant. Particular attention to be paid to the effect of impurities in raw materials, build-up of products in recycle systems, maloperation and equipment failures'.

In 1968 D.M. Elliott and J.M. Owen of Mond Division described the use of critical examination for generating alternatives in the early stages of design, as suggested in Section 2.7[9]. Even earlier, in 1960, D.S. Binsted described a similar application in ICI Organics Division[10]. However, these applications of critical examination never became as popular as hazop, perhaps because they were before their time but more probably because, compared with hazop, they were too cumbersome and time-consuming.

The ICI Central Work Study Department in London played a part in integrating the Mond and HOC forms of the developing hazop technique and spreading knowledge of it throughout the company. A report by G.K. Cooper dated November 1964 brings out clearly the difference between hazop and critical examination:

'Suppose one significant word in the description of a process is "Stirred", and take the guide-word Eliminate, ie No Stirring. In a normal [critical] examination of the process one would be looking at the necessity to stir, and recording possible advantages and disadvantages of not doing so. In Hazard Investigation [that is, what we now call hazop], on the other hand, one is seeking possible causes of such a situation (eg motor not switched on; motor burnt out; paddle blades broken; etc), and what hazards to personnel, plant, or product might happen as a result of it (eg intense local heating with off-spec. product and loss of batch; possible risk of explosion; if product coagulates plant may have to be stripped down; etc).'

Later, the report said:

'A Hazard Investigation affords a means of producing on paper in a systematic and thorough fashion, and in advance of plant start-up, potential hazards to the plant, process and personnel, and of making recommendations to eliminate the hazards. Where the Company policy demands that plants be built with minimum capital expenditure and with minimum sparage [number of spares], and yet with immediate high outputs on start-up, the the need for Hazard Investigation becomes obvious.'

Reading this report over 25 years later, the need for a better Company policy seems equally obvious.

ICI Pharmaceutical Division adopted hazop enthusiastically and the first use of the technique outside ICI occurred in 1967 when R.E. Knowlton (then in Central Work Study Department) led a study for Ilford Ltd[8]. The first published paper on hazop was H.G. Lawley's 1974 paper from which the example in Section 2.5 has been taken. It was presented at the American Institute of Chemical Engineers Loss Prevention Symposium in Philadelphia the previous year (held, incidentally, in the hotel which later became famous as the site of the first recognised outbreak of Legionnaire's disease) and aroused interest from the outset. Gradually other companies adopted hazop. The first contractor to do so was probably Chemetics International, then part-owned by ICI.

Mond Division later integrated hazop into a six stage hazard study programme extending from the early stages of design through to post-commissioning[11]. Hazop is the third stage (see Section 1.1).

7.2 HAZAN

The use of numerical methods for determining standards and priorities in safety was pioneered in the nuclear industry, especially by F.R. Farmer[1,2].

The use of these methods in the chemical industry dates back to the design and construction by ICI HOC Division in the 1960s of two plants in which ethylene was oxidised by oxygen in the vapour phase; one plant was for the manufacture of vinyl acetate and the other for the manufacture of ethylene oxide. Both had to operate close to the flammable limit and it was obvious that, if the concentrations of the reactants departed only slightly from operating conditions, a serious explosion could result. Protection by blast walls was impracticable and the Instrument Design Group were asked if the plant could be made safe by instrumentation. It was at once realised that:

(a) Instrumentation can be designed to reduce the chance of an explosion to any desired level, but zero is approached asymptotically and can never be reached. Therefore:

(b) It is necessary to define the level of safety to be achieved.

The first attempt to define the level of safety stated that working on the oxidation plants should be as safe as travelling by train. Later this was changed to say that working on the oxidation plants should not be significantly more dangerous than working on an average ICI plant. This change meant a slight increase in the safety standard[3].

To design an instrumented safety system to achieve this standard, the methods described in Chapter 3 had to be used. The design has been described by R.M. Stewart, the engineer responsible for it[4].

At the time Stewart was designing the protective systems for the oxidation plants, I was independently trying to apply numerical methods to a range of other problems and produced standards similar to Stewart's[5].

Also, at about the same time, an electrical engineer in HOC Division, V.F. Lord, was trying to find a rational basis for deciding when Zone 2 (then called Division 2) electrical equipment could be used instead of the more expensive and difficult-to-maintain flameproof Zone 1 equipment. So-called 'non-sparking' Zone 2 equipment does not spark in normal use but can spark if a fault develops, typically once in a hundred years. The chance that this will coincide with a leak is small as a Zone 2 is, by definition, one in which a leak of flammable gas or vapour is not likely to occur under normal conditions and, if it does occur, will exist for only a short time. Lord suggested that a Zone 2 area should be one in which flammable gas or vapour is present for less than 10 hours per year and, if so, it can be shown that the FAR for a plant operator from this risk is less than 0.2 (see Section 3.4.1)[5]. Other workers arrived independently at similar conclusions[12].

During the 1970s hazard analysis was applied to many chemical industry problems by many workers, outstanding among whom were S.B. Gibson and H.G. Lawley.

Although Stewart was, I believe, the first person to undertake a detailed hazard analysis of a chemical industry problem, the origins of hazard analysis go back a long way. In any engineering structure the load (L) and strength (S) are not precisely defined but vary about a mean value. Failure may occur if L is a maximum when S is a minimum. However large we make S, complete safety is never achieved but is approached asymptotically. If we know L and the variation in L and S and can define an acceptable failure rate, we can fix a design value for S. The first use of statistical techniques in this way was Chaplin's study of iron chains in 1880[13].

In 1939 Pugsley and Fairthorne[14] pointed out that it was possible, from historical data, to calculate the probability that the forces acting on an aircraft would exceed the design loading, due to gusts of wind and other causes. They then continued, ' ... in present-day civil flying the critical accident rate at which the general public passes from acceptance to opposition is of the order of 1 accident per 10^5 flying hours ... it is suggested that the critical rate for structural accidents in civil flying may be taken as of the order of 1 accident per 10^7 flying hours. This is, of course, only a rough estimate for the purpose of further argument'.

Hazard analysis is based on similar principles to the technique of operations research developed during the 1939–45 war as 'a scientific method for providing executives with a scientific basis for decisions' [15]. Thus it showed that aircraft would be more effective when used on anti-submarine duties than on bombing Germany, and that larger convoys would result in fewer ship losses.

In the postwar years numerical methods were adopted in many fields in which they had previously been little used. Thus an obituary of A.V. Hill, the medical statistician who, in 1952, first showed the connection between smoking and lung cancer, said that he 'had a great impact on a profession that had hitherto dismissed quantitative values'[16].

REFERENCES IN CHAPTER 7

1. Farmer, F.R., June 1967, *Atom*, 128: 152.
2. Farmer, F.R., 1971, Experience in the reduction of risk, *Symposium Series No. 34*, Institution of Chemical Engineers, Rugby, UK, 1971, 82.
3. Kletz, T.A., 1977, What are the causes of change and innovation in safety?, *Proceedings of the second international symposium on loss prevention and safety promotion in the process industries*, Dechema, Frankfurt, 1.
4. Stewart, R.M., 1971, High integrity protective systems, *Symposium Series No. 34*, Institution of Chemical Engineers, Rugby, UK, 99.
5. Kletz, T.A., 1971, Hazard analysis — a quantitative approach to safety, *Symposium Series No. 34*, Institution of Chemical Engineers, Rugby, UK, 75.
6. Gould, S.J., 1987, *An urchin in the storm*, Norton, New York, 52.
7. Cianchi, M., 1988, *Leonardo's machines*, Beocci Editore, Florence, Italy, 12.
8. Knowlton, R.E., 1989, The widespread acceptability of hazard and operability studies, *13th international symposium on the prevention of occupational risks in the chemical industry, Budapest, August 1989*.
9. Elliott, D.M. and Owen, J.M., 1968, *The Chemical Engineer*, No. 223, CE377.
10. Binsted, D.S., 16 January 1960, *Chemistry and Industry*, 59.
11. Turney, R.D., February 1990, *Process Safety and Environmental Protection*, 68 (B1): 12.
12. Benjaminsen, J.M. and Wiechen, R.H., 1968, *Hydrocarbon Processing*, 47 (8): 121.
13. Pugsley, A.G., 1966, *The safety of structures*, Arnold, London, (quoted by Tait, N.R.S., 1987, *Endeavour*, 11 (4): 192).
14. Pugsley, A.G. and Fairthorne, R.A., May 1939, *Note on airworthiness statistics*, HMSO, London.
15. Blackett, P.M.S., 1962, *Studies of war*, Oliver and Boyd, Edinburgh, 169, 173 and 210.
16. *The Daily Telegraph*, 23 April 1991.

CONCLUSIONS

All human activities involve some risk. It can be reduced but not eliminated completely.

Hazard and operability study (hazop) is now a mature technique for identifying hazards without waiting for an accident to occur (Chapter 2).

Hazard analysis (hazan) is now a mature technique for estimating the probability and consequences of a hazard and comparing them with a target or criterion (Chapters 3–5).

Taken together the two techniques allow us allocate our resources so that we deal with the biggest problems first and in the most effective way. Neither technique will be effective, however, unless there is a commitment to safety at all levels (Chapter 1).

Cost-benefit analysis is less well-established so far as safety is concerned, but nevertheless has a part to play (Sections 3.4 and 3.9).

Hazard analysis and cost-benefit analysis are difficult subjects to explain to the public but nevertheless we should try to do so. The hazards of technology should be balanced against the benefits (Sections 3.4 and 5.3).

ADDENDUM — AN ATLAS OF SAFETY THINKING

In his *Atlas of management thinking* (Penguin Books, London, 1983) Edward de Bono says that simple pictures can be more powerful than words for conveying ideas. His book is a collection of what he calls 'non-verbal sense images for management situations'. 'The drawings', he says, 'do not have to be accurate and descriptive but they do have to be simple enough to lodge in the memory. They should not be examined in detail in the way a diagram is examined, because they are not diagrams. They are intended to convey the "flavour" of the situation described'.

In the following I have tried to express the ideas of this book in similar, simple drawings in the hope that they may stick in people's memories rather better than they have done when they have been expressed in words. They are not as abstract as de Bono's diagrams but nevertheless may help us to recall the concepts described in this book.

(1) IDENTIFY — WHAT CAN GO WRONG?

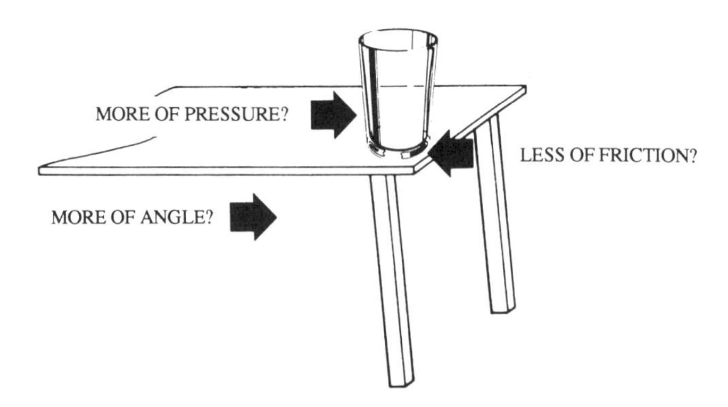

The first and most important stage in any hazard study is to identify the things that can go wrong and produce accidents or operating problems. It is little use studying small hazards if we have failed to realise that bigger ones are round the corner.

(2) HOW BIG WILL THE CONSEQUENCES BE?

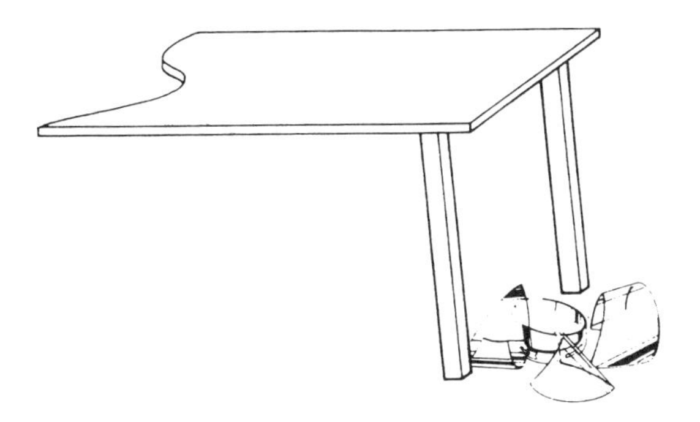

We need to know the consequences to employees, members of the public, plant and profits, now and in the long term. The best way of finding out is to look at past experience but sometimes there is no experience and we have to use synthetic methods.

(3) HOW OFTEN WILL IT OCCUR?

We need to know how often the hazard will occur. Again, the best way is to look at past experience but sometimes there is no experience and we have to use synthetic methods.

(4) PREVENTION

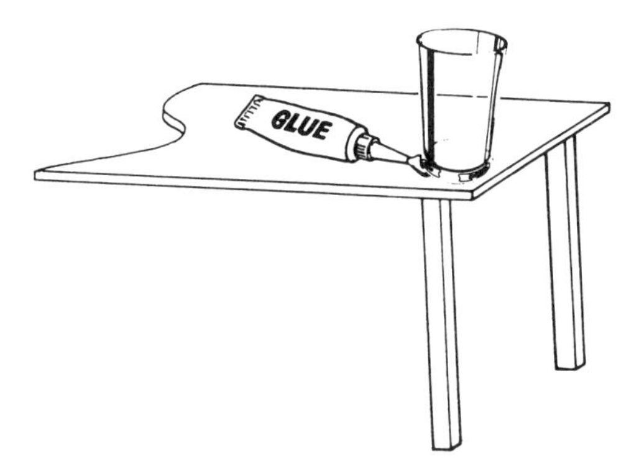

How can we prevent the accident occurring, or make it less probable or protect people from the consequences?

(5) WHAT SHOULD WE DO?

We should compare the risk (that is, the probability times the consequences) with generally accepted codes and standards or with the other risks around us.

(6) IS IT WORTH THE COST?

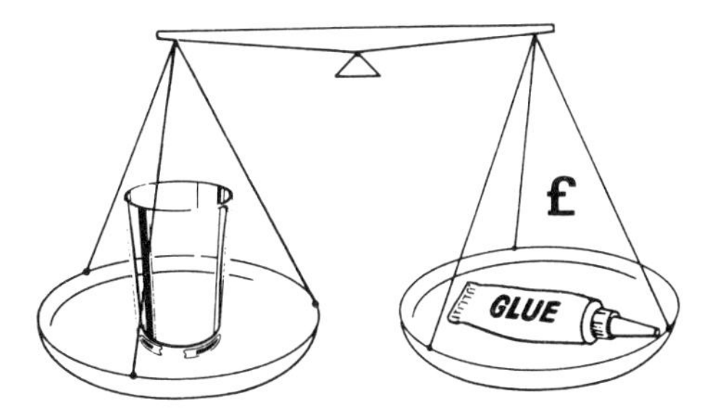

We should also compare the cost of prevention with the cost of the accident in order to see if the remedy is 'reasonably practicable' or if we should look for a cheaper solution.

(7) PREVENTION 2

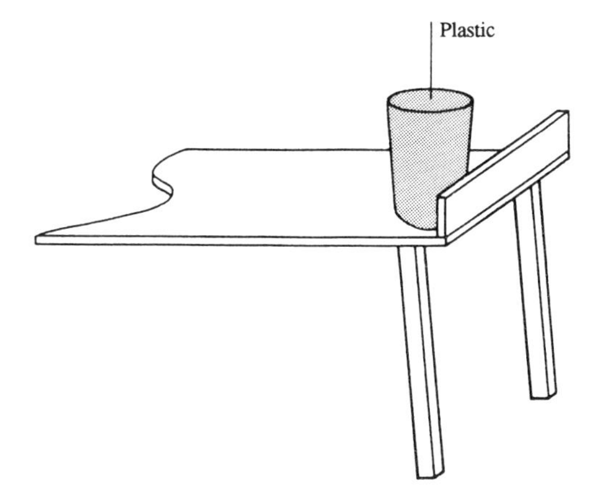

Perhaps our method of prevention has disadvantages. Perhaps we can think of better methods. We should answer this question before the table is made or the glass ordered.

INDEX

A

acceptability criteria 2, 54–71
access 10
accident consequences 121
accident content (of products) 70
accident probabilities 121
accidents, fatal 59–61, 66–67
acid 136
Acts of God 123
aircraft 63, 139
airlines 124
alarms 3, 43, 44, 93–94
algebra 107
alternatives 30, 134
arithmetic 106
asbestos 119
assessment of hazards 1–5, 34–35, 52–132, 144
associations 125, 126
audits 4, 116
automatic restart 85, 110

B

batch processes 14, 29–30, 43–44, 95
bellows 87, 132
belt and braces 88, 103–105
Bhopal 1, 30–31, 39, 40, 113, 124, 126
blinding (see slip-plating)
blowdown 50
brakes 74
branches, small 34
bursting discs 77, 98

C

cancer 124, 126, 139
Canvey Island Report 110
cars 74, 82, 85, 87, 93
cars (see also driving)
cash machines 93
catchpots 34, 98
chains 139
check lists 2
check valves (see non-return valves)
chemical industry 124, 125
Chernobyl 124
clocks 44
closed shop 113
Club of Rome 108
coal dust 119
codes of practice 2, 116
commissioning 4
common mode failures 88–91
complexity 17
compressors 34, 92
compromises, ineffective 90–92
computer control 14, 15, 43–44
computers 26–29, 27
conflict 16
consequences of an accident 2, 7, 54, 99, 132, 143
construction 4, 18, 132
contractors 15, 20, 21
cost-benefit analysis 57, 68
cost of saving a life 67–69, 97
costs (see expenditure)
creativity 17, 27
critical examination 30, 36, 134, 137
criticality 49–50

D

dams 125, 126
data on failure rates (see failure data)
demand rate 71–84
design 52, 89–93, 132
design (see also hazard and operability studies)
deviations 8, 20, 25, 27, 30, 36, 44, 134
dimerisation 24–26, 27
disease, industrial 116–119
distillation 48
diversity 59, 83, 88, 94
driving 122, 123, 124
driving (see also cars)
drugs 122, 123
duration 82

E

eggs 87
emergency isolation 115
environment 70
ethylene 1, 39, 95–97
ethylene oxide 1, 39, 115, 138
expenditure 31, 52–53, 56, 100, 130–131, 134
experience 2, 21, 50, 52, 54, 116, 119, 131
explosions 39, 40, 41, 42, 44, 45, 54, 108, 138
explosive limit 1
exposure 63, 124

F

fail-danger 71, 72, 82–84
fail-safe 71, 82–84
failure data 80, 85–87, 109–111, 115, 130–133, 139
failure mode and effect analysis (FMEA) 36
failure rate 71–86, 93
fairness 125
fatal accident rate (FAR) 96–97
fault trees 77–83, 107
filters 136
fires 40, 50, 54, 91, 108, 115
Flixborough 1, 70
flowsheets 4, 29–32
F–N curves 64–66, 130
food 121, 122, 123, 124
food processing 35
fractional dead time 72–84, 88, 96

G

gaskets 10
gates 78–80
guide words 7, 8

H

handrails 56
hazard analysis (hazan) 1–5, 20, 34–35, 52–132
- acceptability of results 120
- accuracy 119–120, 131–132
- assumptions 109, 132
- comparison with experience 113
- errors in 74, 80, 84–95, 100, 106–113
- examples 95–100
- history 138–139
- introduction of 4
- limitations of 128
- objections to 115–129
- pitfalls 74, 80, 84–95, 100, 106–113
- quality 119
- reasons for 52
- recommendations 112

hazard and operability studies (hazop) 1–50, 97–98, 114
- actions 20
- benefits of 37
- by computer 26–29
- examples 24–26, 39–50
- history 134–138

introduction of 4, 32–33, 114, 116
limitations of 29–32, 50
objections to 21, 114
of genetically modified organisms 36
of laboratory design 36
of mechanical problems 36
of nuclear power plants 36
over-enthusiasm in 20
preliminary 29–32
recording 12–13, 17–19, 26
teams 15–17
timing 18, 114
hazard rates 61, 71–84
hazard studies 4, 138
heart disease 124
Heinrich 66
hoses 136
Hoxha 87
human error 45, 86, 93–95, 111–112, 115–116, 132
human reliability 86, 93–95, 111–112, 115–116

I
identification of hazards 1–50, 80, 108–109, 114–115, 32, 142
incident rate 71–84
India 126
India (see also Bhopal)
innovation 2
instructions 14, 21
blanket 44
instruments (see alarms and trips)
instruments, costs of 25
Irwell, River 48

J
joints 85

K
knock-on effects 24
knowledge 21, 50
ragbag of 17, 45

L
laboratories 36
layering 48–50
lightning 63
liquid hammer 25
load and strength 139
lubrication 132

M
maintenance 84, 85, 87, 115, 132, 133
preparation for 10, 33, 40–41
management competence 3, 87, 109, 111, 116, 123
management judgement 120–121
Manchester Ship Canal 48
materials of construction 85, 87, 95–97
messengers 125
methane 44, 45
methods (see procedures)
method study 134
mixing 8
models 115
errors in 107–108
modifications 4, 20, 21, 41, 42, 50
morality 124, 125
multiple casualties 61

N
non-random demands 76, 93
non-random failures 92–93
non-return valves 33, 92
nuclear power 84, 116–119, 122, 123, 124, 125

nuclear power (see also radioactivity and criticality)
nuts and bolts 10

O
open shop 113
operations research 139
operator error (see human error)
operator reliability (see human reliability)
outrage 124
overfilling 71–74, 91–92
overpressuring 71–73, 78, 78–79
oxygen 1

P
parallel systems 76–77, 131
perception of risks 62
pesticides 121, 123
phenol 134
pipeline fracture 25
pipelines 7, 14, 24, 45–48
pitfalls in hazan 74, 80, 84–95, 100, 106–113
poultry 87
pressure 8, 14
prevention 7, 144–145
priorities 57, 58, 59, 60, 62, 116
probabilistic risk assessment (PRA) 3, 5
probability of an accident 2, 54, 55, 71–84, 99, 103–105, 143
procedures 20, 21, 24
protective systems 40, 95–98, 104, 115, 138
protective systems (see also alarms and trips)
publicity 125
public opinion 120–121
pumps 24, 25, 30, 33, 39, 41, 44, 45, 85, 91–92, 110, 115

Q
quantitative risk assessment (QRA) 3, 5

R
radioactivity 45–48, 49–50, 116–119, 126
radioactivity (see also nuclear power)
radon 122
railways 106, 128
random failures 72, 92–93
rapid ranking 116
reaction kill system 97
reactors 39, 41, 43, 48, 97–98
reasonably practicable 57, 67, 68
redundancy 46, 59, 83, 88, 94
relief valves 40, 57, 58, 71–74, 76, 77, 82, 109, 115, 130, 136
resource allocation 53–54, 100, 116, 121
reverse flow 7, 24, 26, 33, 39, 92, 136, 144–145
risk analysis 3, 4, 53
risk assessment 3, 5
risk criteria 55, 103–105, 138
risk perception 121
risks,
- acceptable 57
- alternatives 70
- familiar 123
- natural 122
- negligible 57–58
- to the public 63–69
- tolerable 57–58
- under our control 122
- versus benefits 124
- voluntary and involuntary 63, 122

risk targets 55, 103–105, 138
rock-climbing 122
runaway reactions 48

S
sabotage 40
safety consciousness 3

Sellafield 45–48
series systems 77, 131
service lines 34, 39, 40–41
settling 8, 24, 25, 45–48
Seveso 14
ship collisions 99
shut-down 8, 11, 21
slip-plating 10
smoking 122, 139
software (see procedures)
spectacle plates 10
spokesmen 125
start-up 8, 11, 21, 44
Stephenson, George 106
storage 24, 25, 31, 40

T

tanks 24, 26, 33, 39, 40, 45, 71, 83, 91–92, 99, 136
targets 56, 67
temperature 8, 14
testing 109, 112, 132
test interval 71–84
tests (of alarms, relief valves and trips) 71–74, 88
tolerability criteria 2, 54–71
top events 78
toxic gas 54
toxic gas (see also Bhopal)
transport 57, 108
  road 70
trips 3, 33, 34, 35, 57, 58, 71–74, 76, 82, 84, 88–92, 95-97, 109, 136
  frequent demands on 74

U

units 81, 107

V

vacuum breaking 136
values 121
valves 10, 93–94
vending machines 85
vessels 71, 73, 78–79, 130
  operation in 34
victims 125
vinyl acetate 138
voting systems 84, 88

W

water 40, 42, 48–49, 50
Weibull analysis 93
Windscale 126